PARACELSUS

ESSENTIAL READINGS

Nicholas Goodrick-Clarke
was educated at Lancing College and
the University of Bristol. He gained
his D.Phil. at Oxford for a thesis in
German history, subsequently
published as *The Occult Roots of
Nazism* (1985).
He has a wide-ranging interest in the
history of ideas and is Series Editor of
the ESSENTIAL READINGS.

PARACELSUS

ESSENTIAL READINGS

Selected and translated by

NICHOLAS GOODRICK-CLARKE

First published 1990

Selection and introduction
© NICHOLAS GOODRICK-
CLARKE 1990

British Library Cataloguing in
Publication Data

Paracelsus, *1493-1541*
Paracelsus.
1. Medicine
I. Title   II. Goodrick-Clarke, Nicholas
III. Series
610

ISBN 1-85274-066-3

*Crucible is an imprint of The Aquarian
Press, part of the Thorsons Publishing
Group, Wellingborough, Northamptonshire,
NN8 2RQ, England.*

Printed in Great Britain by Mackays
of Chatham, Kent
Typeset by MJL Limited, Hitchin,
Hertfordshire

1 3 5 7 9 10 8 6 4 2

ESSENTIAL READINGS

The *Essential Readings* series is designed as an introduction to the thought and work of major figures in the history of ideas, particularly in the realm of metaphysics and the esoteric tradition. This anthology of Paracelsus' writings is an important addition to the series. Paracelsus has remained a legend from his own times down to our own; his name appears in almost every standard history of magic, alchemy, and occultism; and he is regarded, with varying degrees of justification, as the founder of modern medicine and a pioneer of homoeopathy.

The image of the heaven-storming magus bent over his vessels and furnace, surrounded by great tomes filled with arcane knowledge, astrological symbols, and strange sigils, immortalized in the Faust plays of Marlowe and Goethe, is directly inspired by the life and work of Paracelsus. But there is also another Paracelsus, or rather many—the Renaissance naturalist of the two worlds, the macrocosm and the microcosm; the adventurer and traveller in all the lands of Europe; the boisterous iconoclast of the learned academies; the charitable physician ministering to the poor and humble; the brave emissary in towns stricken by the plague; and the lonely figure wandering in the vast snowy wastes of the Alps and preaching the gospel in remote Swiss villages. Paracelsus was a voyager into new realms of science, plumbing the realities of God and man, form and purpose, the very well-springs of Nature and the cosmos.

Despite the legendary fame of Paracelsus, his writings have

remained little known. This is largely due to the difficulties of the language in which he wrote. Long available only in the original Early New High German and Latin, his works were chiefly accessible to those who could read them. This anthology is based on his major medical, philosophical, religious and political, and magical and cabbalistic texts and enables the reader to follow their sense and argument. It is intended to bridge a long-standing gap in our knowledge of the man and his works.

NICHOLAS GOODRICK-CLARKE
March 1989

CONTENTS

ACKNOWLEDGEMENTS

While preparing this anthology of Paracelsus' writings and writing the introduction I have benefited from lively discussions with my wife, Clare, whose own work on Reformation concepts of man examines major trends in intellectual history from early Renaissance neo-Platonism into the seventeenth century. I am also grateful to Dr Charles Webster, formerly Director of the Wellcome Unit for the History of Medicine at Oxford, for reading my manuscript and offering comments.

I also owe thanks to the librarians and staff of the British Library, the Theosophical Society in England, London, the Taylor Institution Library, Oxford, and the Bodleian Library, Oxford.

INTRODUCTION

A

THE LIFE OF PARACELSUS

Paracelsus was a dominant and controversial figure in sixteenth-century medicine, philosophy, and theology. Today he is celebrated as the first modern medical theorist, the founder of iatrochemistry, homoeopathy, antisepsis, and modern wound surgery. He rejected the book-learning and scholasticism of ancient and medieval medicine in favour of a new medicine based on experiment, observation, and new philosophy. Nature and man, not ancient texts, were his sources: he believed that a pious Christian faith, the evidence of his own senses, and a system of correspondences between the macrocosm and the microcosm surpassed the knowledge gleaned from the writings of Hippocrates, Galen, and Avicenna. He saw the philosopher-physician as a guide in the realm of Nature, an explorer in the divine totality of the heavens, the earth, and man. His astrological, alchemical, and occult insights were rooted in the contemporary philosophy of Renaissance neo-Platonism, natural magic, and cabbalism. His radical approach to healing and medicine, his popular style and contempt for professional exclusivity and incompetence provoked the hostility of established authorities everywhere. He was called the Luther of physicians on account of his strident opposition to existing medical practice, coupled with a demand for change and reform. His tireless quest for knowledge, his extensive journeys throughout Europe, the prodigious volume of his writings, and the recurrent cycle of fame and success followed by antagonism forc-

ing him to travel on again, have created a legend around
Paracelsus which persists down to our own day.

Philippus Aureolus Theophrastus Bombastus von Hohenheim, called Paracelsus, was born at Einsiedeln, the important
monastery village and place of pilgrimage in the canton of
Schwyz in Switzerland, in 1493. His father, Wilhelm Bombastus
von Hohenheim, was the illegitimate son of a nobleman and
knight-errant from Swabia, while his mother was a bonds-
woman of the great Benedictine abbey in the village. Their only
child was christened Theophrastus; the other names were
attributed only later and it was not until 1529 that he used the
name Paracelsus, probably to signify 'surpassing Celsus' (the
Roman writer on medicine), by which he is best known. His
mother died when he was still young, and in 1502, as a result
of the Swabian wars, father and son moved to Villach in Carinthia, which Paracelsus described as 'my second fatherland, next
to the country of my birth'. Here Wilhelm von Hohenheim
practised medicine, a respected member of the community, for
the rest of his life. He encouraged his son's interest in natural
history and taught him the rudiments of medicine. Paracelsus
probably attended the monastery schools of St Paul and St
Andrae near Klagenfurt. Lastly, the local mining school of the
Fuggers and their metal ore mines at Paternion, Bleiberg, and
Hutenberg near Villach offered both father and son a rich field
for chemical and medical observation and speculation. Here,
and later as an apprentice in the mines of Sigmund Füger at
Schwaz in Tyrol, Paracelsus received a strong impetus towards
alchemy and his vocation for natural science and medicine.

Besides the scanty notes in Paracelsus' own writings, little
is known of his early life, education, and travels. He identified
among his tutors four bishops and Johannes Trithemius, abbot
of Sponheim (1461-1516), a famous cabbalist. As regards his
education after the monastery and mining schools, Paracelsus
probably studied for a bachelor's degree at Vienna between
1509 and 1512. Determined to become a physician, Paracelsus
then journeyed to Italy and began studying at Ferrara in 1513.
Here he heard the lectures of Johannes Menardus (1462-1536),
an opponent of astrology in medicine, and Nicolaus Leonice-
nus (1428-1524), the medical humanist and critic. Paracelsus

concluded his studies and received his doctorate at Ferrara in 1516. Although he mentioned many of the famous German, Italian, French, and Spanish universities in his work, it seems likely that he only visited them in the course of his later travels; moreover, Paracelsus was generally critical of academic medicine and its scholastic exegesis of ancient Greek and Arabic texts.

Paracelsus sought a universal knowledge, a knowledge that was not to be found in the books or the faculties. The young doctor now embarked on a series of extensive travels around Europe. Between 1517 and 1524 these wanderings led him from Italy across France to Spain and Portugal, through France again, then to England, Germany, Scandinavia, Poland, Russia, Hungary, Croatia, across to Italy and thence to Rhodes, Constantinople and, possibly, Egypt. During this period he enlisted as an army surgeon and was involved in the wars waged by Venice, Holland, Denmark, and the Tartars. Now Paracelsus was motivated by the practical experience of surgery and the great wealth of local and traditional medical folklore among the herb-women, bath attendants, peasants, gypsies, and magicians encountered in the course of his travels.

Paracelsus' life was indeed unconventional from the outset. Initially he had been tutored by ecclesiastics, some with pansophic and cabbalistic interests, while his practical bent inclined him towards natural history, medicine, and mining. He had then studied at universities, first in the general arts and then for his doctorate in medicine. But his studies were not followed by academic preferment or settling down to practise. Instead, he spent almost a decade travelling far and wide in pursuit of more knowledge, while practising the artisan trade of surgery. However, these were turbulent times: new continents were being discovered, traditions and faith were under challenge from the new learning of the Renaissance, and population and new trade and industry were expanding across Europe. Paracelsus' early life reflects the energy and restlessness of this era, whose innovation and change offered a rich harvest of experience to anyone prepared to travel and observe a wider new world.

Paracelsus wanted to found a new medicine which would merge its academic and artisan traditions of learning and practice. This unconventional ambition was his destiny, the principal motive and cause of his chequered career. In advocating a unified medical science, Paracelsus was striking against the strong professional codes and vested interests of physicians, surgeons, and apothecaries. In late medieval Europe physicians were learned scholars and it was beneath their dignity to attend at the sick-bed; on the other hand, barber-surgeons were merely plying a parochial and humble artisan trade, uninformed by theory. Apothecaries made a good living from the herbal remedies of Galen and Avicenna, still upheld by the scholar-physicians. Thus Paracelsus' medical reforms represented a threat to all these groups, making his life a series of fateful clashes wherever he attempted to settle down and practise.

In the course of 1524 Paracelsus returned from his wide-ranging travels that had lasted seven years to his Carinthian homeland. After visiting his father at Villach and finding no local opportunity to practise, he settled down as a physician in Salzburg. Since 1519/20 he had been working on his first medical writings, and he now completed these as *Elf Traktat* and *Volumen medicinae Paramirum*, which describe eleven common maladies and their treatment and his early medical principles. At the same time, Paracelsus felt a deep sympathy for the downtrodden common people, as confirmed by his later religious and socio-political writings. His ethical speculations were in line with those of the Brethren of the Free Spirit, the Anabaptists, and other sectarian exponents of radicalism and popular pantheism in the late Middle Ages and on the eve of the Reformation. At Salzburg in 1525 Paracelsus supported the cause of rebellious peasants, was arrested, and only narrowly escaped the death penalty. He fled westwards, visiting the spas of Swabia and Baden along the Danube, where he studied the thermal waters and their healing virtues.

In December 1526 Paracelsus arrived at Strasburg and entered his name in the town register. He was thus entitled to permanent residence and free to join the guild of surgeons and tradesmen. Although there was an acrimonious dispute with a surgeon called Wendelin Hock, Paracelsus seems to have enjoyed popularity and respect at Strasburg. Most important for him was his contact with the influential circle of Protestant reformers at Strasburg, including Nicolaus Gerbelius, Kaspar Hedio, Wolfgang Capito, and Johannes Oecolampadius, the famous reformer at Basle. Paracelsus successfully treated Hedio, who was the close friend of Capito, the leading light at Strasburg. Capito, in turn, introduced Paracelsus to the humanist circles of Basle. From the middle of January until the end of February 1527, Paracelsus visited Basle. The centre of the humanist movement here was the publisher Froben. Paracelsus stayed at his house, effected a successful cure of his long-standing leg ailment, and became acquainted with his friends Erasmus of Rotterdam and the Amerbach brothers. Although Paracelsus was a Roman Catholic, his friendship with progressive circles and sympathy for the Reformation, his medical proficiency, and his opposition to medieval scholastic medicine commended him alike to humanists, reformed churchmen, and the public. Oecolampadius, the Protestant theologian, was highly influential in the Basle town council and secured the appointment of Paracelsus as town physician in March 1527.

Paracelsus spent only ten months at Basle, but this period marks both the climax and the crisis of his life. The post of town physician was a municipal appointment, but it also carried the commission and right to lecture at the university. This prospect held great appeal for Paracelsus, who sought an audience for his ideas on the new medicine. However, the university authorities had not been consulted over his appointment, and Paracelsus irritated them further by refusing to submit to the formal act of reception as an external graduate. Instead, he challenged the university by issuing an iconoclastic manifesto, the *Intimatio*, in which he promised to lecture daily for two hours on practical and theoretical medicine, not after Hippocrates and Galen (the recognized academic authorities), but on the basis of his own experience and work. Next, on 24 June (St John's Day), Paracelsus contributed to the student rag festivities by burning publicly the fat volume of Avicenna, the canon of scholastic medicine. The faculty reacted by disputing his right to lecture and sponsor doctoral candidates. Paracelsus lodged a protest with the town council and simultaneously complained about the bad practices of the apothecaries, thereby ensuring himself more enemies. The town council supported him and he continued to lecture on such subjects as tumours and wounds, purges, uroscopy, pulse diagnosis, and his work *De Physiognomia* before large and enthusiastic audiences, which included both students and non-academic barber-surgeons. In a further break with tradition, Paracelsus gave many of his lectures in German rather than Latin, an unprecedented practice at the universities in his time and obviously intended as a popular challenge to the exclusivity and elitism of academic medicine.

In these lectures Paracelsus was forming the nucleus of his medical system during a highly fruitful phase of his life. However, his antagonizing of the faculty led to a bitter harvest. His position at Basle was seriously undermined by the death of Froben in October 1527. A damaging lampoon soon followed, ridiculing Paracelsus' terminology and extolling the wisdom of Galen against the 'Cacophrastus' (from the Greek *kakos*, bad) Paracelsus. Again Paracelsus complained to the town council (December 1527) but this time the complaint was shelved. A further incident hastened his fall. When Paracelsus cured a rich church dignitary, who had offered him a colossal reward of a hundred guilders, the patient paid only a small sum. Paracelsus complained, as a matter of principle, to a court, which awarded him just a modest fee. Paracelsus was incensed and accused the magistrate of ignorance and injustice, thereby laying himself open to arrest and severe punishment. On the advice of his few remaining friends, Paracelsus left Basle secretly in early February 1528. Thus ended his great period of promise and rejection, honour and disgrace.

Deeply disappointed by his experiences at Basle, Paracelsus set off on a renewed series of travels in southern Germany, Switzerland, and Austria. During his period of restless wandering from town to town, which filled the remaining fifteen years of his life, Paracelsus was to write and complete many major books on medicine, philosophy, and theology. From Basle he travelled via Colmar and Esslingen, arriving at Nuremberg in 1529. Paracelsus had great expectations of this flourishing centre of commerce, art, and religious reformers. However, his reputation preceded him and the physicians closed ranks against him. Paracelsus provoked them further by offering to cure any patient deemed incurable and promptly succeeded with nine out of fifteen lepers. He also antagonized the Lutheran circles in the city by disassociating himself from Lutheran reforms, for he believed in an extreme formulation of the independence of free will and was an advocate of the common people. But his bitterest quarrel at Nuremberg concerned his book on syphilis, then known as the French Disease, which was newly introduced from the West Indies, causing a fierce epidemic. Contemporary treatment consisted of mercury or a preparation of the American guaiac or pock wood, which was ineffective but brought substantial revenues to the Fuggers of Augsburg, who held the guaiac import monopoly. Paracelsus had already written a critical treatise on the guaiac remedy, and in 1529 he had printed the first volume of an ambitious eight-volume work on the French Disease. Once again Paracelsus was threatening powerful vested interests in his pursuit of medical science. It was an unequal battle: he was forced to leave Nuremberg and his pioneering work was banned by the censors.

Paracelsus now sought peace in the small country town of Beratzhausen, where he entered his most productive phase of medical literary activity. Firstly, he wrote the *Paragranum* (1529-30), intended as a book 'beyond the grain'. In this he demanded that medicine should be based on four pillars: natural philosophy, Astronomy (the relationship between man and the heavens), Alchemy (the science and preparation of chemical remedies), and Virtue (the inherent power of the particular individual, doctor, patient, herb, or metal). The book was introduced by the famous prefaces bristling with vigorous polemics against traditional medicine and its scholastic high priests. In Beratzhausen Paracelsus also resumed religious preaching, which he had practised earlier in Salzburg. He continued preaching at St Gallen, where he stayed next. Here he completed his great *Opus Paramirum*—the 'work beyond wonder'—in 1531. This book contains Paracelsus' mature medical theories, including expositions of his theory of three substances (Sulphur, Salt, and Mercury), a chemical system of medicine which Paracelsus substituted for the ancient doctrine of the four elements; the processes of digestion and nutrition; the nature of women; the matrix (womb), sexuality, and reproduction; diseases due to 'tartar' (stone); psychic phenomena and illnesses arising from the imagination. He dedicated the work to Vadianus, the humanist and former Rector of Vienna University, now acting mayor of St Gallen. Paracelsus benefited from Vadianus' introductions, effected many successful cures, and stayed in St Gallen for more than two years. At this time he also began his writings on comets and other heavenly signs of 1531 and 1532. Close to Protestant thinkers and critical of the Papacy, Paracelsus regarded these phenomena as apocalyptic signs and warnings from God concerning man's wars and wickedness.

Yet again his restless nature drove him onwards. In 1533 he wandered as a poor lay preacher and healer among the Swiss peasants of the Appenzeller country. During this period of retreat in the snowy Alps and the rude villages he wrote many of his short theological and socio-political treatises, including *Liber prologi in vitam beatam, De religione perpetua* and *De ordine doni*. After many months in the mountains of Tyrol he reached Innsbruck clad as a beggar. From here he visited the familiar mining districts of his apprenticeship at Schwaz and wrote his work on the Miners' Disease—the first treatise in medical literature to recognize and analyse an occupational disease. By 1534 he had crossed the Brenner Pass and in June he reached Sterzing (Vipiteno). The small town was in the throes of the plague, which Paracelsus had already encountered during his earlier travels. With no reward he worked courageously among the poor, sick, and dying, bringing relief as best he could with his remedies. He also wrote a little book about his experience with the disease, its diagnosis, and a series of counsels regarding its treatment and a number of prescriptions. He presented this to the mayor but received scant acknowledgement from the town authorities, who were probably mistrustful of his threadbare appearance and practical involvement.

Paracelsus now proceeded southwards to Meran, where he came into contact with a religio-social revolutionary group of Anabaptists, before making his way into the Veltlin (Valtellina), which he praised as the healthiest region in all Europe. He also commended the spring waters of St Moritz for their beneficial effect upon gout and the digestion. From St Moritz he went to Bad Pfäfers, spending the summer of 1535 at the monastery there. He devoted a special pamphlet to the healing properties of the thermal springs in this spa town. Together with his earlier studies of the spas in Swabia and Baden, this medical work establishes his reputation as the founder of balneology. Before leaving the monastery Paracelsus wrote a short consilium for the abbot, Johann Jakob Russinger.

Journeying northwards again, he left his native Switzerland and travelled through the Allgäu district of Bavaria via Isny, Kempten, and Memmingen, arriving in Ulm at the beginning of 1536. Here he arranged for the printing of his great work on surgery, *Die grosse Wundarznei*, on which he had been working for several years. However, the work did not progress to his satisfaction, so he entrusted the task to Heinrich Steiner at Augsburg (July–August 1536), who brought out the first and second books. The work was an immediate success and was reprinted a year later. In the same months he also published his *Prognostication for the next 24 years*, a book of political and religious predictions, which he dedicated to his patron King Ferdinand I of Austria, the brother of the Emperor Charles V. From Augsburg he travelled by way of Nördlingen, Munich, and Passau to Mährisch Kromau, where he had been invited to a consultation with Johann von der Leipnik, a high dignitary of the Kingdom of Bohemia. As a patron of persecuted Protestant sects in Bohemia, Leipnik took a strong interest in the philosophical ideas of his physician. He invited Paracelsus to stay on at Kromau as his guest and advance his written works. Paracelsus accepted this offer and began his great philosophical opus *Astronomia Magna or the whole Philosophia Sagax of the Great and Little World* (1537–8). This presented a systematic account of Paracelsus' scientific world-view based on the macrocosm–microcosm correspondences of Renaissance neo-Platonism, including his classification of nine members (branches of knowledge) in each of the four varieties of Astronomy, which he understood as the study of the totality of the heavens and the earth.

After his stay at Mährisch Kromau, Paracelsus visited Pressburg (Bratislava), where a ceremonial dinner was held in his honour at the end of September 1537. At this time he appears to have recovered the reputation and wealth which he had either lost or forgone during this Swiss and Tyrol period. At his next sojourn in Vienna he was even granted two audiences with King Ferdinand. But in the midst of these successes there are still reports of strife with authorities and a series of disputes with the Austrian treasury. In May 1538 he returned to his old home town, Villach, and dedicated his 'Carinthian trilogy' to the estates of the archduchy. This trilogy comprised a chronicle of Carinthia, the medical work *Labyrinthus medicorum errantium*, and an *apologia pro vita sua*, the *Sieben Defensiones*. The dedication was graciously acknowledged by the estates and an early printing promised. Now Paracelsus wandered in the 'desert region' around St Veit and Klagenfurt, while completing *Philosophia Sagax*. By now his health had broken down, so that, exceptionally, he declined to travel to a consultation with a nobleman in Pettau (Ptuj). In late 1540, however, aid seemed to be at hand, for he was invited to settle at Salzburg by the bishop suffragan, Ernst von Wittelsbach. But Paracelsus was not granted a lengthy respite. Following a stroke on 21 September 1541 at Salzburg, he dictated his will, bequeathing his modest possessions of a little money, some clothing, and biblical scripture to the poor. He died on 24 September 1541.

B

THE PHILOSOPHY, MEDICINE, AND THEOLOGY OF PARACELSUS

Paracelsus was a pioneer of the new Renaissance world, which rediscovered man and his power in the universe. He broke with the closed hierarchial structures of medieval thought and determined to explore and describe the natural world. His enterprise was inspired by the Renaissance neo-Platonic conception that the whole of creation—the heavens, the earth, and all Nature—represented a macrocosm, and that its unity was reflected in a variety of possible microcosms, of which man was the most perfect. The analogies and correspondences between the macrocosm and the microcosm were central to his cosmology, theology, natural philosophy, and medicine. Such analogical speculation was present in Greek philosophy and throughout the Middle Ages, but Paracelsus was the first to apply this approach systematically to the study of Nature. These neo-Platonic ideas also underpinned his theory of knowledge. Paracelsus expressed a deep distrust of logical and rational thought as a scientific tool. Since man was the climax of creation, uniting within himself all the constituents of the world, he could have direct knowledge of Nature on account of a sympathy between the inner representative of a particular object in his own constitution and its external counterpart. For Paracelsus, this union with the object is the principal means of acquiring intimate and total knowledge. Moreover, this true knowledge does not concern the brain, the seat of conscious rational thinking, but rather the whole person.

Paracelsus was above all a naturalist. He set out to explore how Nature works and to discover the eternal laws by which it is governed. The work of Nature consitutes a visible reflection of the invisible work of God. Nature thus provides signs by means of which God grants a glimpse into His secret wisdom and design. Paracelsus' conception of Nature was rooted in his cosmological and theological ideas. Whereas God had created natural objects such as stars, herbs, and stones, He did not create their 'virtues' (essential activity or power). Prior to all creation these uncreated virtues had always been in God; in the course of creation they were distributed in the natural world as direct emanations of God. Just as all virtues in natural objects are divine and supernatural, so human ability and wisdom are also gifts from God. Paracelsus thus exhorts man to 'seek, knock and find' and further his knowledge of Nature as a religious duty to understand the work of God. The wonders of God, the cures, and the arcana (secret remedies) are lavished upon the natural world all around us. Nature can reveal these signs of God. The naturalist is engaged in an empirical search for the divine seals in Nature.

This empirical search was a mode of enquiry quite opposed to the medieval concern with an intellectual mastery of ancient authorities and traditional texts. Paracelsus contrasted his own notions of experience and science with that pseudo-knowledge based on logic and reasoning, an elaboration of abstract categories and models of reality bearing little relation to the actual objects, influences, and events in the external world. He rejected scholatic book-learning and its slavish dependence on the old ideas and systems of Aristotle (384-322 BC), Galen (c. 129-199), and Avicenna (980-1037). In accordance with Gnostic ideas, Paracelsus conceived of all creation having two sides: a visible elemental (material) part and an invisible superelemental (astral) part. Man, the microcosm, likewise possesses a carnal elemental body and an astral body (*corpus sidereum*) which 'teaches man' and is able to communicate with the astral part of the macrocosm, the uncreated virtues or direct emanations of God in the world of Nature. He saw experience as a process of identification of the mind or astral body with the internal knowledge possessed by natural objects in attaining their specific ends. The researcher should try to 'overhear' the knowledge of the star, herb, or stone with respect to its activity or function. Science is thus already present as a virtue in the natural object, and it is the experience of the researcher which uncovers the astral sympathy between himself and the object. This identification with an object penetrates more deeply into the essence of the object than mere sensory perception. Paracelsus' science is both profound and holistic in its approach to Nature.

Magic was an essential part of Renaissance neo-Platonic philosophy, first exemplified in the influential works of Marsilio Ficino (1433-99). Magic in this context does not mean the cultivation of demons, but the capture and direction of the divine virtues in natural objects for the benefit of man. This 'natural magic' was fundamental to Paracelsus' world-view and science. Firstly, magic reveals the invisible influences between things, providing the basis of medicine, philosophy, and astronomy. Secondly, magic is an action or practice, by means of which the magus can bring heavenly forces down to earth, into himself, or on to other objects, which thus acquire the power of the transferred virtue, be it from a star, a plant, a gem, or any other natural object. The magus requires a strong mind in which the heavenly and earthly forces are balanced and combined. His power is spiritual and superior to matter and the elements. He becomes at least the equal of Nature and can achieve wonders with the aid of the virtues he has mastered. The magus can also transmute objects, transfer power, act at a distance, and predict events. Impressed by Ficino's idea of the priest-physician, Paracelsus saw the physician as a magus who knows all the virtues of herbs, minerals, and other objects. By a process of concentration the physician can capture the virtues of Nature in a miniscule remedy, for such an extract 'has many leas and meadows in its fist'.

Paracelsus' insistence on the union of researcher and object and his belief in natural magic strike the modern mind as subjective. Scientific thinking prides itself on an 'objective' attitude and demands distance and disassociation between observer and object. Since the time of Galileo (1564-1642), Descartes (1596-1650), and Newton (1642-1727), science and philosophy have typically striven for separation, distinction, and measurement in order to demonstrate the differences between objects and phenomena. By contrast, mystical and magical modes of thought seek similarities, sympathies, and 'wholes' in Nature and the cosmos. Paracelsus' notion of experience, his advocacy of homoeopathy, his doctrine of 'signatures' (whereby the form of an object symbolizes its virtue or essential action), all indicate a holistic world-view based on the traditions of Gnosticism and the Cabbala. His rejection of abstract reason and logic as a distorted model of reality and his search for similarities and symbolical correspondences between the macrocosm and the microcosm led him towards a more empirical view of Nature and a sensitive apprehension of the world about us. The map is not the territory, but Paracelsus' map certainly represented a closer approximation to Nature than the constructs of medieval philosophy. Moreover, the spiritual relation between man and the cosmos was central to his science of the symbol, whereas this vision was lost in the science of the system from the seventeenth century onwards.

The terms 'astral' and 'heavenly' occur frequently in Paracelsus' account of correspondences between the macrocosm and the microcosm and also in his Gnostic dualism regarding the two sides of creation: visible and invisible; elemental and celestial; carnal and spiritual. Given this constant reference to the *astra* (stars), one may ask how he viewed them. Paracelsus appeared to break with medieval astrology by asserting the limitation of astral powers: individual stars determined neither man's nature nor his behaviour, nor even the length of his life. However, Paracelsus could not dispense altogether with the stars in his scheme of the macrocosm and the microcosm. The visible stars had no causal influence, but their power lay in the heavenly co-ordination and correspondences between objects and phenomena. Once Paracelsus described this astral concordance as a portrait of human affairs in the heavens; also that the heavens represent a 'prelude' (prophecy as opposed to cause) relating to man's life and actions. He noted a correspondence between each planet and a particular seat of disease. He furthermore maintained that the stars could help direct the virtues of remedies to the diseased organ in the body. The physician should thus know how to bring about a concordance between the planet and the remedial herb. However, this subtle distinction between astral action and correspondence is blurred in his *Philosophia Sagax*, where descriptions of astral 'inclination' and 'impression' jostle with notions of free will.

The question whether Paracelsus embraced or rejected astrology cannot be answered simply. But such a question fails to comprehend Paracelsus' new approach to Nature and the essence of Renaissance neo-Platonism. Paracelsus used the term *astrum* to denote not only a celestial body (star or planet), but the 'astral', divine, and invisible virtue or activity essential to any natural object. While ancient and medieval astrology attributed a dominant and causal role to the stars in a strictly hierarchical conception of the cosmos and creation, Paracelsus ushers in a new age by bringing those powers down to earth and distributing them in divine virtues, signs, and seals throughout the natural world. In this way he shifts attention from the traditonal generality of medieval cosmology towards the local, the specific, and the empirical. During the Renaissance man was now looking all around himself to discover the powers of Nature and how it works. Man and Nature consequently enter into an active relationship rather than remaining the passive objects of transcendental power, be this God or the stars above.

Paracelsus developed a theory of matter from these new philosophical ideas. Here again one can see how he moved towards an empirical concern with specifics. Medieval science, largely based on Aristotle and the translations of his works by the medieval Arab philosopher Avicenna, still accorded the four Elements—Earth, Water, Fire, and Air—a pre-eminent position in the theory of matter. The qualities of a substance or an object were deemed to reveal its elemental nature: cold and dry (Earth), cold and moist (Water), hot and dry (Fire), and hot and moist (Air). Although these four Elements still feature in Paracelsus' theory, they are no longer the last and irreducible components of matter. He thought that an immanent, specific, and soul-like force determined the nature and species of an object rather than its (visible) chemical components. For him, substances were but crude envelopes which disguised an underlying pattern of spiritual forces and it was this pattern, not the corporeal cover, which dictated the composition of matter.

Paracelsus generally 'spiritualized' matter, in claiming that such spiritual forces are the true elements and principles, while the Elements and chemical substances are only the crystallized deposits of such forces. Taking the notion of Prime Matter ('Arche' or 'Ousia') from ancient Stoicism, Paracelsus regarded the visible Elements as the results of an interaction between the qualities of heat, cold, moisture, and dryness and this Prime Matter, a kind of vital matter-spirit.

According to Paracelsus, God created things in their 'prime', but not in their 'ultimate' matter. Paracelsus viewed all Nature as in process of transformation, whereby all objects are being perfected. He personalized the principle responsible for this process as Vulcan, an immanent virtue or power which works in the matrices (the traditional Elements) of Air, Earth, Fire, and Water. In this task Vulcan is assisted by two further powers or principles. Firstly, it needs to draw upon a reservoir of energy, which is necessary for the nourishment, growth, and preservation of all natural things. Paracelsus called this general reservoir the *Iliaster*, a type of primordial matter-energy which essentially is and expresses the entire potential of all nature. Secondly, since Vulcan draws upon a general resource, it requires a specific agent to impress the specific and individual attributes upon the elemental material world. This agent was known as the *Archeus*. Paracelsus described both Vulcan and the *Archeus* metaphorically as workmen, craftsmen, and alchemists perfecting prime matter into ultimate matter, whether in Nature at large or in the human body. These concepts show again how Paracelsus was not interested in identifying units of matter, but was searching for the 'intelligences' or *semina* (seeds) in matter, which as *archei* are responsible for all specificity in Nature.

Paracelsus accorded a central importance to Sulphur, Salt, and Mercury as the Three Principles of which all bodies consist. One would be mistaken if one thought that Paracelsus was referring here to the chemical substances known as sulphur, salt, and mercury. He used these terms to denote principles of constitution, representing organization (Sulphur), mass (Salt), and activity (Mercury), all varieties of the specific forms achieved by the immanent intelligences and *semina* of matter. But Paracelsus also used the terms in a chemical context: Sul-

phur represents the combustible, Mercury the smoky or volatile, and Salt the unchangeable component in any natural object.
These principles are disclosed when the elemental cover is
removed. For instance, when a piece of wood is burned one
sees flame (Sulphur) and smoke (Mercury), while only ash (Salt)
remains. These principles of constitution, together with the
complex scheme of intelligences and *semina*, the Vulcan, the
Iliaster, and the *Archeus*, are the dominant concepts in Paracelsus'
theory of matter-energy and the process of life, while the
ancient Elements are relegated to a secondary function as
matrices, vehicles, or even mere covers for the active spiritual
forces.

Ancient Greek medicine, deriving from Hippocrates and
Galen, was based on a theory of the four chief fluids or humours
of the body (blood, phlegm, yellow and black bile), which were
supposed to determine the temperament of the individual. A
predominance of blood over the other humours produced a
ruddy complexion and a courageous, hopeful, amorous dis-
position; too much phlegm resulted in calmness, then sluggish-
ness and apathy; yellow bile or choler caused anger and
irascibility; black bile or melancholy produced introspection,
sadness, and depression. Galen attributed disease to an upset
of the humoral equilibrium, whereby there was an excess or
deficit of one of the humours and the qualities of heat, cold,
moisture, and dryness. Disease was a matter of 'distemper'.
Medieval medicine, represented by the works of Galen and
Avicenna, had built up an elaborate pharmacology of herbal
remedies for numerous degrees of humoral imbalance, based
on logical and rational extrapolations from a limited amount
of original observation. On the one hand, this scholastic medicine produced the remote and bookish physician of the Middle
Ages who expounded theory but did not actually treat patients;
on the other hand, the apothecaries dealt in an endless variety
of herbs and other remedies which had little or no relation to
the disease and often made the patient's condition worse.

The ideas and developments of Paracelsus' theory of matter
are plainly evident in his pioneering medicine. He opposed and
destroyed the ancient humoral medicine and related ideas. He
denied that the four humours and temperaments could explain

the wide variety of diseases. He rejected the paramount importance of the constitution and its internal order in ancient pathology. Instead, Paracelsus developed a medical theory which
related the macrocosm and microcosm, while building on his
dynamic notions of matter and energy. There were two important consequences: firstly, Paracelsus saw disease as something
which affects the body from outside rather than as an internal
imbalance; secondly, this wider relationship between man and
the external world led to a search for specific cures and remedies relating to particular diseases and disorders. Paracelsus also
used chemical remedies, based on his speculations concerning
Sulphur, Salt, and Mercury, with far more promising results
than the effects of the old Galenic herbs. For this reason,
Paracelsus is often hailed as the founder of modern medicine
and iatrochemistry.

In his theory of matter, Paracelsus had invoked the Elements
as matrices in which *semina* could thrive and proceed towards
specific forms. But there is a total sum of species (*Iliadus*) which
can be generated by the principles (Sulphur, Salt, and Mercury)
in any given matrix. Thus there is an *Iliadus* of Earth, Water,
Fire, and Air. But since man represents a microcosmic matrix,
there is also an *Iliadus* of man. Just as the *Iliadus* of an elemental matrix grows 'species' and 'fruits' with the aid of Vulcan
and the *Archeus*, so the human *Iliadus* is liable to produce fruits,
which can bring forth an excess of what is typically integrated
or absorbed in the course of organic bodily processes. Paracelsus' pathology thus rehearses his dynamic theory of matter,
whereby the three principles of constitution can direct conditions in the body in a manner comparable to their operation
in an elemental matrix. Diseases are specific 'species' or 'fruits'
which grow in the organs of the body.

Natural objects and diseases differ according to the interaction of the three principles of constitution with their corresponding matrices. This process of interaction occurs in the
universe, thus generating the myriad species of objects, and likewise in the body, whereby the disease-species are generated.
The same process also generates the herbs and minerals—
typically from the elemental matrices of Earth and Water—
together with their powerful virtues in the world of Nature.

While Paracelsus' new chemical medicine still explains pathology in terms of changes in matter, he is primarily concerned with salt and other chemicals—not as substances but as principles—and their relation to the function, power, or virtue inherent in matter, the body, and the arcana. It is thus the task of the physician to identify and understand these virtues and arcana in relation to a particular disease in a specific organ within the matrix of man. Physicians endowed with the powers of magic and the Cabbala will themselves act as *Archei* in the restoration of health.

The medicine of Paracelsus is mainly represented in this volume by readings from *Elf Traktat, Volumen medicinae Paramirum*, and the *Opus Paramirum*. Here one can deduce his extraordinary advances in medical thinking beyond the formulae and systems of humoralism. Paracelsus propounds a medicine which leads to the localization of disease. He distinguishes diseases according to the different organs affected, their different anatomical changes, and the different exogenous causes. Paracelsus dispenses with the tortuous humoralist theories which are necessary to explain, for example, how black bile from the spleen causes ulcers on the leg. He sees a specific disease and proposes a specific remedy. Since diseases are 'species' or 'fruits' distributed throughout mankind, there is an aetiology or science of their anatomy, causes, and treatments. By contrast, ancient pathology only recognized general 'distempers' and thus employed non-specific remedies such as sweating, bloodletting, and vomiting intended to evacuate any morbid matter. Paracelsus' medicine regards disease not as a constitutional phenomenon but as a parasitic invader; its cure demands the removal of a specific agent. Hence his therapy is not symptomatic but fundamental.

This concern with the local and specific, ideas which flowed naturally from the exploration of correspondences and analogies, led Paracelsus to the isolation of virtues in concentrated extracts and chemical remedies. This new pharmacy is based on a scientific procedure and has less to do with the trial and error of Galenic herbalism and nothing whatsoever to do with the ancient formulae of qualities, grades, and humours. Paracelsus is often called the father of homoeopathy. His chemical

remedies are indeed based on the fine sympathies between the
diseases and the arcana. This sympathy is opposed to the ancient
principle of opposites in remedial action. Paracelsus denied that
a 'cold' remedy can cure a 'hot' disease, unless this is due to
the other properties of the remedies concerned. He claimed that
cancer corresponded to arsenic in the macrocosm and asserted
that arsenic itself would cure this arsenical condition. Similarly,
stone (a hard morbid concretion in the kidney, etc.) can be cured
by other stones such as crab's claws, lapis lazuli, sponges, aetites,
and celenites. A scorpion's venom can cure scorpion poisoning. Paracelsus thought that the specificity of an arcanum lies
in its 'anatomy' or structure, the work of Vulcana and the
Archeus in the particular elemental matrix. Because the anatomy of the remedy is identical with that of the disease agent,
Paracelsus was a staunch advocate of the iso- or homoeopathic
principle in medicine.

Paracelsus' philosophical inspiration led him to expose the
weakness and unreality of elemental and humoral doctrines.
Many important proto-scientific ideas and modern medical theories emerge in his work. His specific contributions to medicine are impressive and include: a humanitarian and ethical
approach towards the patient, especially the mentally ill; a
recognition of the healing power of Nature and the value of
antiseptic principles; progressive views on syphilis and a rejection of guaiac and mercurial treatments; knowledge of the
diuretic action of mercury and its curative powers in dropsy;
the connection between goitre, minerals, and drinking water
in certain places; studies of spa waters and observations of the
beneficial digestive effects of certain acid waters (balneology);
the description of the Miners' Disease as an occupational illness in which he shows the greater toxical risks in metals than
in salts and recounts a concrete aetiology with numerous
symptoms.

Notwithstanding, it is misleading to call Paracelsus the
founder of any particular branch of medicine. These accurate
and valuable insights are embedded in an opus which already
fills twenty volumes in the Sudhoff-Matthiessen and Goldammer editions. His works are chiefly concerned with his system of neo-Platonic correspondences and their illustration by

recourse to analogy, symbol, and myth. These correspondences are empirical details of a universal theory of matter based on spirit, energy and divine purpose. It is not appropriate to understand Paracelsus as a figure at the threshold of modern Western scientific thought. We should rather reflect on the perennial truths of his science of the symbol and their unexpected relevance to the profound problems of our scientific and technological era. He was the founder of an alternative science and medicine.

Alchemy plays a major part in the thought of Paracelsus. Medieval alchemists such as Arnald of Villanova, John de Rupescissa, and the followers of Ramon Lull had already practised an art which was both operative and empirical in that it was based on visible results rather than logic. Their alchemy was primarily concerned with the volatile substances, their protection from evaporation and retention in solid bodies. All motion, activity and form were held to depend upon volatile or spiritual (airy or fiery) principles, which were virtues within objects. Substances were produced in alchemy by a process comparable to generation in Nature. By imitating the natural generation of diverse substances and acting on the humours of metals, alchemy was supposed to be able to convert base metals into perfect metals. Alchemists believed that they could 'cure' and convert base metals into gold by a process of removing their impurities. These ideas seem very similar to those of Paracelsus. He too sought the volatile, the invisible and the virtues inside objects. He compared alchemy to medicine and the baseness of metals to disease.

Paracelsus also followed the medieval alchemists in his rejection of gold-making as the ultimate goal of alchemy. He mainly regarded alchemy as important for the curing of disease and the prolongation of life. Alchemy was another means of perfecting what Nature had left in an imperfect state. Paracelsus based his alchemy on the parallels between the macrocosm and the microcosm and the various possible transformations of the three principles of constitution, the fluid (Mercury), the solid (Salt), and the combustible (Sulphur). Paracelsus quoted Hermes Trismegistus, who stated that all seven metals, 'the tinctures' (generating principles), and the Philosopher's Stone all derive from three substances, namely spirit, soul, and body. Paracelsus claimed that these were identical to his three principles of constitution: Mercury (spirit), Sulphur (soul), and Salt (body). Since Mercury represented the spirit, this metal was as important as gold, the solar metal. However, Paracelsian alchemy treated Sulphur, Salt, and Mercury as principles rather than as the elements of medieval alchemy. Also, Paracelsus used chemical reactions to explain the processes of human physiology; medieval alchemy attempted the converse. Paracelsus developed upon medieval alchemy by focusing upon its naturalistic and medical implications.

In his philosophy and medicine Paracelsus replaced the medieval, hierarchical conception of God, man, and Nature with a more reciprocal and direct relationship between God and man through His presence in man and Nature. Paracelsus regarded human spirit and talent as direct emanations of God. According to this essentially neo–Platonist notion, the spirit is a divine spark of the Godhead which inheres in man. Paracelsus regarded man as the crown of creation and believed in his free will and power to the extent that he could even act upon the stars. Since man had such tremendous potential, Paracelsus could not countenance the subjection of man within an arbitrary social or political structure. He believed that men should be free to develop their gifts to the utmost for communal benefit, rather than being harnessed to the political interests of a master or lord. His motto 'that man no other man shall own who to himself belongs alone' contains an explicit social and political philosophy based upon the notion of the divinely inspired individual.

As a Reformation figure, Paracelsus has often been compared to Luther. They share many traits, including coarse and boisterous language, the use of vernacular German rather than Latin as a popular means of communication, the wholesale rejection of academic predecessors, and theatrical acts intended to appeal to students and common folk such as the burning of books and public instruction. However, Paracelsus was a pacifist and a staunch advocate of the ordinary people. He sided with the rebellious peasants who risked persecution and death in their struggles against the feudal lords at Salzburg in 1525. His medicine was inspired by charitable motives and involved risks to his own health and life. He expressed his Christianity through acts of self-denial and practical works. He was always prepared to take the part of the poor and the downtrodden against the rich, mighty, and privileged. His conviction in the absolute value of each individual's link with God was paramount in his social and political attitude. Whilst inspired by similar motives, Luther ultimately upheld the authority of the secular princes of Germany against the revolting peasants.

In his religious ideas Paracelsus remained committed to theological individualism and popular pantheism. The latter derived from the philosophy of Salomon Ibn Gabirol (1020-70), also known as Avicebron, who described prime matter as a unity of spirit and body in all things inferior to God. David of Dinant (d. 1209) adapted Avicebron's doctrine of prime matter to denote the Godhead which originates, sustains, and exists in all things. The emanationist implications of David's popular preaching reached and influenced many mystical anarchist and millenarian movements in the late Middle Ages, including the Waldensians, the Brethren of the Free Spirit, the Amaurians, the Beghards and the Beguines, the Bohemian Adamites, and the Anabaptists. Paracelsus revived the idea of 'prime matter' in his concept of *Iliaster* and regarded this reservoir of potential matter-energy as necessary for the nourishment, growth, and preservation of all natural things. *Iliaster* is also a spiritual vital force in man and thus justifies his free and independent status in a moral and political context. It is therefore possible to see Paracelsus as an heir of the same popular pantheism which inspired sectarian revolutionaries.

Paracelsus' social and political views were radical, and he is known to have had frequent contact with scattered Anabaptist groups in the 1520s and 1530s. He agreed with the diverse social reformers of his time in their critique of the contemporary powers of Church and State. But it would be wrong to identify him with secular revolutionary thought. His approach was one of balance. Paracelsus was opposed to dogma. He recognized private property within limits, upheld the rights of the individual, and regarded the family as the fundamental unit of society. He also preserved the medieval idea of Christian community life, so that his 'communism' was a matter of natural inspiration rather than systematic, rule-bound, and class-conscious. He interpreted property and poverty as religious and theological states of being rather than as economic privilege and misfortune. He exposed the antisocial and antihuman nature of commercial and professional vested interests. But he was also a conservative and entrusted his proposed plan of communalizing the land and the means of production to the Emperor and his administration.

Paracelsus was bold and uncompromising in his views and proposed reforms. Both the man and his works possess an epic quality, so that it is not surprising that his ideas and influence should have long survived his own lifetime. Indeed, during his life only a few of his writings were published. From the early 1550s onwards more and more Paracelsian texts came to light. The publication of the numerous books, tracts, and papers during the period up to 1570 reflects the activity of the early Paracelsists, including Adam of Bodenstein, Michael Toxites, Gerhard Dorn, Theodor and Arnold Birckmann. The collected editions were first published by Johannes Huser of Waldkirch (Baden) in 1589-91, 1603, and 1605. At the beginning of the seventeenth century Paracelsus gave an important impetus to the Rosicrucian movement and strongly influenced Michael Maier (1568-1622) and the famous Christian mystic Jakob Boehme. Other Continental and English Paracelsists included Oswald Croll, John Dee, Francis Anthony, and Robert Fludd. This period represents the peak of his immediate influence in certain medical circles; by the second half of the century his importance was eclipsed by the primacy of rational empiricism in science and medicine.

During the zenith of rationalism in the eighteenth century Paracelsus was remembered only to be dismissed as a mystical obscurantist whose theories represented an early phase in the development of modern medicine. But Paracelsus' ideas were rediscovered by Goethe, Novalis, Schelling, and other Romantic thinkers at the close of the eighteenth century. His name and works were popularized by H.P. Blavatsky, Franz Hartmann, and Rudolf Steiner in the modern occult revival at the end of the nineteenth century. His ideas concerning the cosmic all-life, the spiritualization of matter, and the divine nature of virtue and energy have emerged in the new philosophies of science of Vitalism and Holism, and in the archetypes of Jungian psychoanalysis. Today, in the new efflorescence of interest in the esoteric and the expanding practice of alternative medicine, one may again detect the perennial ideas of Paracelsus.

MEDICINE

ELF TRAKTAT (*c.* 1520)

1.1

1. DROPSY

When the body begins to swell abnormally from the feet upwards to the hips, genitals, and heart as far as the eyebrows, and it continues to fill up until the spirit of life drowns in the body, as if man were subject to an excessive efflux causing his body to grow folds, there is a tightening around the heart, coughing, shortness of breath. These things are the disease called dropsy. Finally, the urine is reddish in colour, the skin splits open and the fluid runs out, and there is thirstiness. In some people, the disease is quick, in others slow, depending on the impression of the heavens. Death occurs likewise.

In order to understand the causes of the disease one must know these things, the virtue of the heavens, terrestrial nature, and the microcosm—the heavens as a twofold craftsman, visible and invisible; terrestrial nature which is nothing without the heavens; and the microcosm as the patient. The heavens and the earth are twofold, but man is a unity. Take the following example: the earth is nothing without the impression of the heavens. The earth greens, brings forth fruit, and lives through the heavens; that is to say, the heavens are its life, disease, and health. Now there are two earths: terrestrial nature and man, for whom it was created. The man is the invisible earth and yet he has the nature of the earth. The heavens are twofold: the visible heavens work their (visible) impressions on the earth such as rain, dew, frost, and such like, and from these impressions the earth draws life. There is also a hidden heaven which works upon both man and the earth. Since man is an invisible earth, he too requires benefit, and moreover invisible benefit. The influences are like rain, dew, etc., and are impressions comparable to their visible counterparts. Just as the rain can ruin the soil, making it too moist, and drowning it, so man can be saturated. This is dropsy. As the impression saturates the microcosm, so the water sinks by its own weight through the passages of the body, filling them and all other cavities and muscles. Depending on the strength of the impression, the water rises up to the knees, the hips, the genitals, the passages of the stomach, on and on upwards. Because the spirit of life resides in the centre of man, it is in danger of drowning and it cannot flee. Thus is resists and drives the water further on into the upper points of the heart, but the spirit is weakening. In effecting the cure consider three things: the heavens, the earth, and the microcosm. Only the element fire can withstand the heavens' water: that is the sulphur of metals. This sulphur can resist the influences by drying out, for it is the sun which drives away the rain and evaporates it. When the earth is saturated, the superfluity of water must be removed to prevent the earth from rotting. Because rotting is a dissolution which cannot be made whole again, only the element of dryness, which is also a fire, can help here. That is the crocus of metals and there is nothing drier. The cure of dropsy thus consists in these two things, the crocus drying out and the sulphur consuming like the sun.

I. i. 3–8

1.2

2. CONSUMPTION

Consumption occurs when the subtle body or one of its members begins to dry out, either internally or externally, and is thus reduced and loses weight. Concerning the cause of consumption you should understand this: everything which grows on earth has its fatness, size, and thickness, and this measure and weight come from the heavens by means of dew and rain. Thus the earth is obliged to the heavens for everything being in its full and proper measure. Now if the heavens were unfavourable and withdrew this nourishment, things would begin to dry up and wither like hay and die through this aridity.

The body of man comes from the earth and thus he too is subject to this impression. If the heavens are favourable to him, he will have his proper weight; but if they are not, his weight will decline and he will lose up to half or all of his blood, flesh, or internal organs. The man dries out more each day until he is a hard body or a piece of wood which has lost all its sap. Man is so created than the impressions rather than food and drink make him fat or thin. Wherever the impression is totally withdrawn, nothing can green; the food and drink dry up, dry out. The body of man resembles the earth: it is fruitful in summer and unfruitful in winter. Thus, whatever summer has given, winter consumes, and the following summer must make good what has been lost. Winter also befalls man and the former growth is consumed. If another summer did not come, all men would dry out. But as soon as winter is past, the next summer is there, and whatever has been consumed by the winter, grows green again in the summer. This comes about through the virtue of the heavens, and man as the microcosm must bear with it . . . Every impression of the heavens has an invisible effect on men. One should understand the brain, the heart, and every other organ as countries and regions, which require so much rain unless they are to dry out. The four external limbs, arms and legs, can dry out and so can the internal organs. Thus there are consumptions of the heart, liver, spleen, lungs, kidneys, flesh, blood vessels, synovial fluid, joints, nerves, etc., or a general consumption of the whole body. There is a sun in the body which dries and removes moisture. If no rain comes, the sun will dry the body right out and cause consumption.

I. i. 24-27

1.3

When the consumption concerns the heart, there is a shaking in that region; if it concerns the lungs, there is a dry cough, dizziness in the head, a wan face, a thirst in the liver and the kidneys, and a change in the urine; the spleen pricks, the gall bladder burns and itches, the stomach is oppressed, the flesh develops cavities and dimples . . . A general consumption leads to a gradual decrease on account of the slowness of the drying process . . . If the coughing in the lungs passes and there is no more pain in the stomach, but an increase of pain in the bladder, much thirst and hunger, these are signs of a difficult recovery. If these are not affected, then one can hope and expect a good recovery. In effecting the cure, one must consider whether the microcosmic sun is giving enough moisture to replace what it is consuming. Now one cannot compel the heavens to do this, for they are not subject to the desires and appetites of man. However, there is an art of making another heaven in the case of human disease. This is just as powerful as the heavens above in the hands of the physician. Just as the grass grows to cover whole fields, we must sprinkle some water so that it may grow like the grass. This is the arcanum that gives rain and dew in the microcosm and takes away the consumption. Margarita, pearls make women give milk when they are dry, give rain and dew to consumptive limbs, and have a comparable influence to the impression from the heavens above. Thus one should sprinkle what the body needs and the heavens will not provide . . . If this impression of the lower heaven is sprinkled in the form of the pearls, the dew and rain rises and the sun has delight in them in the microcosm. The pearls should be prepared in form of a fluid elixir and one should be careful with the dosage.

I. i. 28-30

[The remaining nine tracts are devoted to the diseases of jaundice, colic, stroke, deaf-mutism, worms, constipation and diarrhoea, gout, epilepsy, and cold sweats and fever. In the case of each disease or condition Paracelsus proceeds methodically, dividing his tract into sections on the disease: its causes (in which the macrocosm-microcosm correspondence plays the paramount part); the course of the disease; contrary and mistaken views regarding the disease; signs and symptoms of the disease; explanation of the disease; and the cure.]

2

VOLUMEN MEDICINAE PARAMIRUM (c. 1520)

2.1

The *entia*, the active principles or influences which govern our bodies and do violence to them, are the following. The stars have a force and efficiency that has power over our body, so that it must always be ready to serve them. This virtue of the stars is called *ens astrorum*, and it is the first *ens* to which we are subjected. The second power that governs us and that inflicts diseases upon us is *ens veneni*, the influence of poison. Even if the stars are sound and have done no injury to the subtle body in us, this *ens* can destroy us; therein we are subject to it and cannot defend outselves against it. The third *ens* is a power that injures and weakens our body even when the two other influences are beneficient; it is called *ens naturale*, the natural constitution. If it goes astray or disintegrates, our body becomes sick. From this many other diseases, indeed all diseases, can arise, even if the other *entia* are sound. The fourth *ens*, the *ens spirituale*—the spiritual entity—can destroy our bodies and bring various diseases upon us. And even if all four *entia* are propitious to us and are sound, yet the fifth *ens*, the *ens Dei*, can make our bodies sick. Therefore none of the *entia* deserves as much attention as this last one; for by it one can recognize the nature of all other diseases ... Note moreover that the various diseases do not come from one cause, but from five.

I. i. 173–4

2.2

The stars control nothing in us, suggest nothing, do not irritate us, incline to nothing, they are free from us and we are free from them. But note that without the heavenly bodies we cannot live: for cold, warmth, and the consummation of what we eat and drink comes from them: but the human being does not. They are as useful to us and we need them as much as we need warmth and cold, food and drink and air: but further they are not in us nor we in them. Thus has the Creator designed. Who knows what there is in the firmament which can serve us? For neither the clarity of the Sun, nor the arts of Mercury, nor the beauty of Venus helps us; but the sunshine helps us, for it makes the summer when the fruit ripens and those things that nourish us grow. But observe, if a child, which has been born under the luckiest planets and stars, and under those richest in good gifts, has in its own character those qualities that run counter to those gifts, who is to blame for it? It is the fault of the blood, which comes by generation. Not the stars, but the blood brings that about.

I. i. 180

2.3

One man surpasses another in knowledge, in wealth, or in power. And you ascribe it to the stars; but that we must banish from our minds: good fortune comes from ability, and ability comes from the spirit. Every man has a special spirit according to the character of which he has a special talent, and if he exercises that talent he has good fortune. Understand that this spirit is the *Archeus* and we will not treat of it further lest we wander from our point. You say also concerning the varying stature of men that so long a time has passed since Adam that amongst so many men it is impossible that one should resemble another, with the exception of twins, and that is a great miracle. And you attribute this to the heavenly bodies and to their mysterious powers. You should know that God has decreed a special feminine entity and that until all types, colours, forms of mankind are fulfilled, and these are innumerable, people will be born who will be as the dead have been.

When the last day comes, then will all the types and fashions of men he fulfilled, for only then will the point be reached when all colours, forms, types, and fashions of men are at an end and no new fashion can be created. And do not imagine that you can make the world older, or any part of it. For when all the forms and fashions of mankind have been fulfilled and no new type can be called into being, the age of the world is at an end.

I. i. 181-2

2.4

You say, and rightly, that if there were no air, all things would perish. But the air is held in the firmament, and if it were not in the firmament, the firmament would melt away, and this we call the *Mysterium*. And observe well that this *Mysterium* contains all created things in heaven and earth and all the elements live in it and by it ... To explain what this *Mysterium* is, note first an illustration. A room shut up and locked has an odour which is not its own, but which comes from whomsoever has been inside. Therefore, whoever goes inside must be sensible of the odour, which is not generated by the air but comes from him who has been in the room. Now understand that we speak of the air in order that we may explain the *ens astrorum*. You allege that the air comes from the movement of the firmament: that we do not stand still, but that the wind proves itself to be meteoric. The air comes from the Most High and was before all created things, the first of all: after which the others were created. The firmament exists by the air as well as all other created things: therefore the air does not come from the firmament. For the firmament is maintained by the air, as man is; and if the firmament stood still, there would still be the air. If the world were to dissolve when the firmament stood still, it would be because the firmament had no air and because the air had melted away, and then all mankind and all the elements must pass away, for all are maintained by the air: that is *Mysterium magnum*. This air may become poisoned and changed and men breathe it in, and since man's life dwells in it, so must his body, which seizes on what is in *Mysterium magnum* and taints itself therewith. Just like the air in the room, there is some-

thing which taints the *Mysterium*, remains in it and cannot escape
from it.

I. i. 182-4

2.5

But that is how you should understand the *ens astrorum*. The
stars have their own nature and properties just as men have upon
the earth. They change within themselves: one sometimes better, sometimes worse, sometimes sweeter, sometimes sourer,
and so on. When they are good in themselves no evil comes
from them; but infection proceeds from them when they are
evil. Now observe that the stars surround the whole world just
as a shell does an egg: the air comes through the shell and goes
straight to the earth. Then observe that those stars which are
poisonous taint the air with their poison, so that where the
poisoned air comes, at that place maladies break out according to the property of the star: the whole air of the world is
not poisoned, only a part of it according to the property of
the star. It is the same too with the beneficent properties of
the stars: that too is *ens astrale*: that is the vapour, exhalation,
exudation of the stars mingled with the air. For thence came
cold, warmth, drought, moisture, and such like according to
their properties. Observe that the stars themselves do not act:
they only infect through their exhalations that part of the *Mysterium* by which we are poisoned and enfeebled. And in this
matter the *ens astrale* alters our body for good or evil. A man
whose blood is hostile to such exhalations becomes ill; but one
whose nature is not hostile is not hurt. He too who is finely
fortified against such evils suffers nothing, because he over-
comes the poison by the vitality of his blood, or by medicine
which combats the evil vapours from above. Observe then that
all created things are opposed to men, and men are opposed
to them: all may hurt men and yet men can do nothing to them.

I. i. 184-5

2.6

A fish-pond which has its right *Mysterium* is full of fish; but
if the cold becomes too great it freezes and the fish die, because

the *Mysterium* is too cold opposed to the nature of the water. But this cold comes not from the *Mysterium*, but from the heavenly bodies whose property it is. The heat of the sun makes the water too warm and the fish die on this account also. Certain heavenly bodies affect these two things, and others make the *Mysterium* acid, bitter, sweet, sharp, arsenical, and so on, a hundred various flavours. Every great change in the *Mysterium* changes the body, and so note how the stars contaminate the *Mysterium*, so that we fall ill and die of natural exhalations. No doctor need wonder at this, for there is as much poison in the stars as on the earth. And he must remember that there is no disease without a poison. For poison is the beginning of every disease and through the poison all diseases, whether in the body or occasioned by wounds, become disclosed. You will discover if you recognize this, that more than fifty diseases, and fifty more besides not one of which is like another, are all due to arsenic: still more are due to salt, still more to mercury, still more to red arsenic and sulphur. We point this out to you to make you realize that you may seek in vain for the special cause of one particular illness, so long as one substance gives rise to so many: find out the substance and you will then find out the special cause. And hold fast to the rule that you must know the substance which has caused the malady rather than the apparent cause, as practice will prove.

I. i. 185–6

2.7

Observe that some of the *entia astralia* poiscn the blood only—such is red arsenic; some hurt only the head, as mercurial poisons; some only the bones and blood vessels, as salts; some are of such a nature that they produce dropsy and tumours, as orpiment or flowers of arsenic; some produce fevers, as the bitter poisons. That you may fully understand this we will show you how maladies are divided. Observe that those *entia* which go into the body and there encounter the *liquorem vitae* produce maladies in the body: others produce sores and wounds and are those which encounter *virtutem expulsivam*. All theory is contained in these two.

I. i. 187

2.8

Now that we have explained the *ens astrale*, we will show you the *ens veneni*, which causes us to fall ill ... You know that our bodies require a constitution, by means of which they are maintained and nourished, and where this is absent, there is no life ... There is no poison in the body, but there is poison in what we take as nourishment. The body is perfectly created, but food is not. Other animals and fruits are our food, but they are also a poison to us. They are not poisonous in themselves, they are perfectly created as we are. But they are poisonous to us as food—that which is poisonous to us is not poisonous to them.

I. i. 189

2.9

Because everything is perfect in itself, but both a poison and a benefit to another, God employed an alchemist, who is such a great artist at dividing the two from each other, the poison into his sack, the goodness into the body ... Just as a prince knows how to employ the best qualities of his servants and to leave the others alone, so the alchemist uses the good qualities of our food for our nourishment and expels those things that would harm us ... The ox eats grass, man eats the ox. The peacock eats snakes and lizards, animals complete in themselves, but not good for food except for the peacock ... Every creature has its own food, and an appropriate alchemist with the task of dividing it. The ostrich has an alchemist to separate its excrement from its nourishment. The salamander eats fire and he needs his own alchemist. The pig will eat human excrement because the alchemist of the pig is more subtle than the alchemist of man and can still separate nourishment from the excrement. Pig excrement is eaten by no animal because there is no cleverer alchemist to extract the nourishment than the alchemist of the pig ... The alchemist takes the good and changes it into a tincture which he sends through the body to become blood and flesh. This alchemist dwells in the stomach, where he cooks and works. The man eats a piece of meat, in which is both bad and good. When the meat reaches the stomach, there is the alchemist who divides it. What does not belong to health he casts away to a special place, and sends the good wherever it is needed. That is the Creator's decree; thus is the body maintained that nothing poisonous eaten shall affect it. That is the virtue and power of the alchemist in man.

I. i. 189-90

2.10

A poison is concealed beneath the goodness in everything which man takes as his nourishment. That is to say, there is an *essentia* and a *venenum* in everything: the *essentia* supports him, the *venenum* causes him illness ... For sometimes the alchemist does his work imperfectly and does not divide the bad from the good thoroughly, and so decay arises in the mixed good and bad and there is indigestion. All maladies from the *ens veneni* arise from defective digestion. But where the digestion is disturbed, the alchemist is not in full possession of his instruments and corruption follows, and that is the mother of all such maladies, for it poisons the body ... Pure water can be tinged to any colour and the body is like that water and takes the colour of decay, and there is no colour of decay which has not its origin in poison.

I. i. 195-6

2.11

Ens naturale is this: in astronomy you know the influence, the firmament, and all the heavenly bodies, and how to explain the stars, planets, and the nature of the heavens down to the smallest detail; there is an identical constellation and firmament in man. We should not mind calling man the microcosm, but you should understand this correctly. Just as the heavens with their firmament and constellations are free and independent, so man is constituted completely independently without any linkage. Thus there are two creations: one in heaven and earth, another in man ... The earth brings forth all the fruits, in order that man can live on them. But all the fruits that grow in the world, grow in man. The earth is only there to bear fruits and nourish man. The body also has this function. All the nourishment necessary for the limbs grows out of the body itself, and such growth is similar to the fruits of the earth. But you should understand that the body nourishes only four limbs; the others are planets and require no nourishment. For the body is twofold: heavenly and terrestrial. Man has two natures within him: the self-nourishing and that requiring nourishment. There is a part of the body which requires no external nourishment, that is the heaven in the body. But the *corpus* which resembles the earth gives of itself to nourish the four limbs. But man also has a connection, in that he must take nourishment from outside: this nourishment serves only the *corpus*, as manure does a field. It introduces no fruit, nor does it increase his seed, but simply maintains his substance and makes him lustful. That is how nourishment is useful to man.

I. i. 202-4

2.12

There are seven organs in the body which require no nourishment but are self-sufficient like the seven planets which nourish themselves, taking nothing from each other, nor from the stars. Jupiter is such a planet, which needs no manure for the maintenance of its body, for it received adequate provision at its creation. And likewise the liver requires no manure . . . And just as Jupiter and the liver are to be understood, so the brain is the Moon, the heart the Sun, the spleen Saturn, the lungs Mercury, and the kidneys Venus. In the same way that the heavens have their motions, so you must understand the natural movement in the body. If you do not understand this, you cannot induce a crisis in the natural diseases caused by the *ens naturale*.

I. i. 205

2.13

When a child is born, his firmament and the seven autonomous organs like the planets are simultaneously brought into being . . . At the time of birth this firmament of the child acquires predestination—that is, how long the *ens naturale* will run for. Take the example of an hourglass which one sets up and allows to run. As soon as it begins, you know the time it will end. Nature also knows how long the *ens naturale* will run. And throughout its duration the *ens naturae* and *creati* will cause all the circuits of the bodily planets to be completed in the period between creation and the predestined end. If a child is predestined to live but ten hours, its bodily planets will complete all their circuits, just as they would if it had lived for a hundred years. The bodily planets of a centenarian, on the other hand, perform exactly the same number of circuits as those of a child which survives an hour, only at a slower rate.

I. i. 206

2.14

Thus it is wrong to correlate the crises by which the body may cure its disease arising from the *ens naturale* with the stars and their motions. What disease the body contracts by its *ens naturale*, the body purges by crises according to its own circuits and not those of heaven. According to the *ens naturale* Saturn has nothing to do with the spleen, nor the spleen anything to do with Saturn. One should count from birth until the predestined end and leave the heavens to do their own business. If someone knew the predestination of the heavens, he would know the predestination of man. But only God knows the predestination, that is, the end. But note that the climaxes, conjunctions, oppositions, and such like do not occur in a material sense, but spiritually, in the general type of organization rather than in bodily changes. For the speeds of the bodily circuits do not admit of any increase or decrease of substance . . . Astronomical time is long, human rhythms are short.

I. i. 207-8

2.15

Now that we have discussed the motion of the stars and the elements of the physical body, we will describe the four humours: choleric, sanguine, melancholic, and phlegmatic. However, we will dismiss the traditional teaching that these derive from the stars or the elements. Thus, there are in the body, as in the earth, four flavours: sour, sweet, bitter, salty.

These four flavours inhere in everything, but they can only be established in man. The choler originates in bitterness and everything which is bitter, and is hot and dry. Melancholy is sourness, for everything which is sour is cold and dry. Phlegm comes from sweetness, for what is sweet is cold and moist. Sanguine is from salt; whatever is salty is sanguine, hot and moist. These are the four humours to be found in the body. When salt predominates in the individual, he is sanguine; when the bitter predominates, he is choleric; the sour, melancholic; the sweet, phlegmatic. There are four humours, but only one predominates . . . With regard to these observations about the motion of the body, there are four bodily circuits: the heavenly, the elemental, the complexions, and the humours. All diseases deriving from the *ens naturale* may be divided into four types: the sidereal, namely chronic diseases; the elemental, that is acute or severe illness; the type of the complexions, that is *morbi naturales*, natural diseases; and the type of the humours, that is diseases of colour.

I. i. 211-14

2.16

There are two kinds of disease, one material affecting the body, the other immaterial in the spirit. The latter cannot be physically grasped and is invisible, but it can suffer from all diseases just as the body can. The cause of these is called the *ens spirituale*, for the reason that the body has nothing to do with it. But do not forget that when the spirit suffers, so does the body, for it manifests itself in the body . . .

I. i. 216

2.17

There are both body and spirit, and the purpose of the spirit is to maintain the body, just as the air prevents creatures from suffocating. The spirit of man is substantial and visible, tangible and sensitive to other spirits. They relate to other spirits, just as the body does. I have a spirit, another man also has one, and the spirits know each other as I do another man, they converse with each other, not through our speech but through their own. It is possible that two spirits may become angry with each other and one hurts the other. This injury will occur in the spirit, but as the spirit is in the body, the body will suffer and fall sick, not physically as a result of a physical *ens* but in the spirit, for which a spiritual medicine is appropriate.

I. i. 217

2.18

There are two ways in which the spirit can cause disease in the body. Firstly, when the spirits injure each other, without any will or thought on the part of man; in the second case, one should note that it is possible to hurt another by the unified force of thought, feeling, and will. This determined and directed will is a mother of the spirit ... If I desire to hurt another with all my will, this will-power is a creature of my spirit and acts against the spirit of the one concerned. He will suffer physically, and yet this pain does not come from the body but from the spirit. Likewise, there can be a fight between the two spirits and one will overpower the other and win. If my opponent succumbs, this is due to his spirit not being so ardently inflamed against me as is mine against him.

I. i. 219-20

2.19

You know that if a wax image of another person is buried and weighted with stones, then that person will suffer pain in the places where the stones lie and will not recover until the image is unburdened. If a leg is broken in the image, then that person will also break his leg; the same applies to stabs, wounds, and other things. This is the power of necromancy ... it is a matter of the spirit of one person being injured by the spirit of another. The body does not receive the wounds, although it feels them and they become visible. The spirit is causing it. You should not therefore treat the body but the spirit, so that the body may recover ... You should also know that many can be made ill through the power of will without the aid of figures, images, and that kind of medium. This can occur in the case of people unversed in these matters who are so strong-

willed that they can inflame and bring illness to the spirit of
another. This happens through the medium of their sleep,
whereby their dreams of the other are fulfilled, the spirit of
one comes to the other in sleep and causes an injury through
the medium of words which are not consciously registered.

I. i. 220-3

2.20

We wrote the first four books of this work in a heathen idiom,
and now we want to write the fifth book about the *ens Dei*,
so that we cannot be accused of being heathen. This is an
account of the heathen usage proceeding in accordance with
Nature and what God has predestined for us. However, just
as diseases derive from Nature and the four *entia*, we should
seek their treatment in religious faith and not in Nature, as the
fifth book will show. Thus you should know that you should
seek the whole basis of healing in the fifth book, where the
true medicine is demonstrated.

I. i. 225

2.21

All health and disease comes from God and not from man. The
diseases of man must be divided into two groups: the natural
and the purgatorial. The natural diseases come from the first,
second, third, and fourth *entia*, the fifth is the chastisement.
God gives us a punishment, an example or lesson made manifest
in our diseases, in order that we may see that all our knowledge
is nothing . . . But in order that we may learn the reason, God
gives us medicine for our diseases, as well as health and illness. One should note that all our diseases ought to be cured
in their own time and not according to our desire and will.
That is to say, no physician can know the period of our recovery, for God holds that in his hand. For every disease is a
chastisement, therefore no physician can heal it, until this
chastisement is ended by God. The physician should be one
who works in the consciousness of predestined chastisement.
Considering that every disease is a chastisement, a physician
should reflect that he cannot determine the hour of recovery

nor the hour of his medicine's effectiveness. The physician can be as good or as artful as he may wish, but the hour of the end of the chastisement must first come. God created medicine to combat disease, and also the physician, but he denies them both to the patient, until the hour has come when Nature and art can take their course. Not until the time has come, and not before.

I. i. 226-7

2.22

God will do nothing without men. If he works a miracle, he does it through men, namely through the physicians. But since there are two kinds of physicians, those who heal miraculously and those who heal through medicine, understand above all that he who believes works miracles. But because faith is not so strong in all men, and yet the hour of chastisement comes to an end, the physician accomplishes that which God would have done miraculously had there been faith in the sick man.

I. i. 228

2.28

For the true art is reason, wisdom, and sense, and sets in order the truth which experience has won; but those who hold to fantasy have no ground to stand on: only formulae that are past and done with, as you know well enough.

I. i. 234

3

DAS BUCH VON DER GEBÄRUNG DER EMPFINDLICHEN DINGE IN DER VERNUNFT (c. 1520)

3.1

We will divide the propagation of all created things into two categories. First, in the case of insensible creatures like foliage and grass, stone and ore, and other things, the seeds for their procreation are found mixed and embedded in the essence of their nature, and are inseparable from it. Second, the sensible creatures like man and the beasts have no seeds which spring from their nature. But here we are exclusively concerned with man. Neither a man nor a woman possesses seeds for the procreation of their species; they are without seeds and free in nature, while all the insensible creatures are mothers and carry seeds. Man is free without the embedded seeds and does not procreate as other creatures.

I. i. 252–3

3.2

God created all things, but man alone He placed in the light of Nature to be free and independent. Because of the eternal in man, God took away his seeds and his instinct... He created man and woman and gave neither seeds, in order that lust might not lead them out of the light of Nature. But in order that they could procreate He gave them free will to decide whether they wanted to or not and thus he planted the seed in their imagination. Thus, if a man wants to procreate, this speculation creates

the desire, and the desire creates his seed. . . God placed the
seed in the speculation and gave free will to the speculation,
to decide whether it had desire or not. But this desire does not
arise from his nature but must be kindled by an object. That
is to say, when a man sees a woman, she is the object, and it
depends only on him whether he follows this object or not.
For God endowed man with reason, in order that he might
know what the desire means. But he himself must decide
whether to yield to it or not, whether to follow his reason or
not. God has placed the seed in man's speculation, in which
his reason lies, and in the object which kindles the speculation. But man must decide that he wants to, otherwise there
is no seed in him. It is the same with woman. When she sees
a man, he becomes her object and her speculation begins to
dwell on him: she does this by virtue of the reason which God
has given to her. She has the power to feel desire or not. If she
yields, she becomes rich in seeds; if not, she has neither seed
nor desire. Thus God left the seed to the free decision of man,
and the decision depends upon man's will. He can do as he
wishes. And since this free decision exists, it lies with both,
with man and with woman. It will happen according the decision of their will. Thus is the propagation of the seed.

I. i. 254

3.3

Both the man and the woman each have a half seed and the
two together make a whole seed. And note how they come
together. There is in the matrix [womb] an attractive force (like
amber or a magnet) which draws the seeds unto itself. . . Once
the will has determined, the matrix draws unto itself the seed
of the woman and the man from the humours of the heart, the
liver, the spleen, the bone, the marrow, blood vessels, muscles,
blood, and flesh, and all that is in the body. For every part of
the body has its own particular seed. But when all these seeds
come together, they are only one seed.

I. i. 261-2

3.4

When the seeds of all organs come together in the matrix, the nature of the matrix combines the seed of the head with the seed of the brain and that of the eye-crystal in its own way and putting each in its proper place, and thus each single organ is placed where it belongs, just as a carpenter builds a house from pieces of wood. Then every seed lies as it should lie in the mother, which is called the microcosm. And all things which make a man are there, save life and the soul... But the seed of a single man is not able to give birth to a man. God wishes to make man out of two and not out of one; he wishes man to be composed of two and not of one alone. This may be considered philosophically: if man were born of the seed of one individual, no other form of man would grow. His child would be just as he is, in the manner of a walnut tree, which is reborn of itself alone and therefore is like the one from which it is born. In all trees, the same always comes from the same, just as walnut trees all bear the same nuts and nothing changes. The same is true of man. If he had been born only of one individual, he would be like his father, and this father would be his father and mother in one. Thus there would be only one kind of people, and each would look like the other, and all would have the same seed and the same nature. But the mixing of the seeds of man and woman produces so many changes that no individual can be like the other. Each individual's seed breaks the other's seed and that is why no man is like another.

I. i. 262-3

3.5

When the matrix has received the seeds, Nature combines the seeds of the man and the woman. The stronger and better of the two seeds will form the child or its chief characteristics. For example, the seed from the man's brain and that from the woman's brain make together only one brain; but the child's brain is formed according to the one which is the stronger of the two, and it becomes like this seed but never completely like it. For the second seed breaks the first, and this always results in a change of nature. And the more different the two seeds are in their innate nature, the more will the breaking and dissimilarity be manifest. Thus the seed of the nose forms the nose in the child, according to the mixed form of those of the parents. The diseases of the parents can be inherited according to whose seed prevails. The more one seed prevails over another, the more the child will resemble that parent.

I. i. 263–4

3.6

God set a term for the development of a child: namely forty weeks; similarly a term was set for the cows, the pigeons, and other animals. During this period the seed develops into a child and in this manner: when conception has occurred, Nature orders the seeds as they should be, the seed of the head moves to the place of the head, the seed of the arms to its place, and every seed to where it should be. When everything is in its right place, the matrix stops and does nothing more. Thereupon follows the action of material nature and makes the child grow, so that everything which has been thus arranged may develop into a body: what belongs to flesh develops into flesh, what belongs to bone into bone, what belongs to blood vessels into blood vessels, what belongs to the internal organs into internal organs. And thus the seed ceases to be seed, and becomes flesh and blood as it should be in a man; then the material nature gives way to God's grace and this gives the child life and every attribute of a living being—sight, hearing, touch, taste, smell— and then it has the virtue of growth. When life has thus been given according to God's dispensation, the child grows in the womb, until all its members gain their full strength, and they are not deficient in nature and virtue, and are quite solid. Once this is so, the child is endowed with spirit, soul, reason, understanding, and all that pertains to the soul... This all occurs in the specified number of weeks. Understand, therefore, how the received seed is at first formed and ordered, then transformed into flesh and blood, then is given size and strength, in order to be able to cope with life on earth; finally, how a maturation of spirit and soul attends this strength. The soul follows the spirit for this reason: it is possible that the growing child may develop into a monster which is of no use to the soul. But if the growth is complete and healthy, then the spirit comes as the herald of the soul, which soon follows. Thus the child grows in the union of spirit and body, until it can no longer do without the earth's air and the maternal food. And then the birth follows.

I. i. 270-2

4

NEUN BÜCHER ARCHIDOXIS (1526)

4.1

BOOK I
CONCERNING THE MYSTERY OF THE MICROCOSM

If, my dearest sons, we consider the misery by which we are detained in a gross and gloomy dwelling, exposed to hunger and to many and various accidents, from all sources, by which we are overwhelmed and surrounded, we see that we could scarcely flourish, or even live, so long as we followed the medicine prescribed by the ancients. For we were continually hedged in by calamities and bitter conditions, and were bound with terrible chains. Every days things became worse with us, as with others who were weighed in the same balance, whom also the ancients have not so far been able to help or to heal by means of their books. We do not in this place advance the different causes of this misfortune. This only we say, that many teachers by following the ancient methods have acquired for themselves much wealth, credit, and renown, though they did not deserve it, but got together such great resources by simple lies. From which consideration we have wished to elaborate and write this memorial work of ours, that we might arrive at a more complete and happier method of practice, since there are presented to us those mysteries of Nature which are too wonderful to be ever thoroughly investigated. Wherefore we have come to consider how that art can be reconciled with the mysteries of Nature, in opposition to those who, so far, have not been able to arrive at the art at all.

The strength of this mystery of Nature is hindered by the bodily structure, just as if one were bound in a prison with chains and fetters. From this the mind is free. For in its operation this mystery is like fire in green wood, which seeks to burn, but cannot on account of the moisture.

Since, then, hindrance arises from this source, one had to see how to get free from it. For such freedom being secured, this art of separation can only be compared to the art of the apothecaries, as light is compared to darkness. And this we say not in mere arrogance, but on account of the great frauds practised by apothecaries and physicians. Wherefore, not undeservedly, we call them darkness, or caves of robbers and impostors, since in them many persons are treated for gain by ignorant men; persons who, if they were not rich, would at once be pronounced healthy, since the practitioners know that there is no remedy or help for these people in their consultations.

This, then, is worthy to be called an art, which teaches the mysteries of Nature; which, by means of the quintessence, can cure a contraction and bring about health in the space of four days, whereas otherwise death would be the result. A wound, too, can be healed in twenty-four hours, which would scarcely yield to bodily treatment in as many days. Let us, therefore, readily approach by experiment this separation of the mysteries of Nature from the hindrances of the body.

First, then, we have to consider what is of all things most useful to man and most excellent. It is to learn the mysteries of Nature, by which we can discover what God is and what man is, and what avails a knowledge of heavenly eternity and earthly weakness. Hence arises a knowledge of theology, of justice, of truth, since the mysteries of Nature are the only true life of man, and those things are to be imitated which can be known and obtained from God as the Eternal Good. For although many things are gained in medicine, and many more in the mysteries of Nature, nevertheless after this life the Eternal Mystery remains, and what it is we have no foundation for asserting, save that which has been revealed to us by Christ.

And hence arises the ignorant stupidity of theologians, who try to interpret the mysteries of God, whereof they know not the least jot; and what it is not possible for man to formulate, namely, the will of Him who gave the mystery. But that word of His they twist to their own pride and avarice; from whence arise misleading statements, which every day increase more and more. Hence it comes that we lightly value, nay, think nothing at all of that reason which is not evidently founded on the mysteries. In like manner the jurists have sanctioned laws according to their own opinions, which shall secure themselves against loss, though the safety of the State be imperilled.

Seeing, then, that in these faculties so many practices have come into vogue which are contrary to equity, let us dismiss the same to their proper time. Nor do we care much for the vain talk of those who say more about God than He has revealed to them, and pretend to understand Him so thoroughly as if they had been in his counsels; in the meantime abusing us and depreciating the mysteries of Nature and of philosophy, about all of which they are utterly ignorant. The dishonest cry of these men is their principal knowledge, whereby they give themselves out to be those on whom our faith depends, and without whom heaven and earth would perish.

O consummate madness and imposture on the part of human creatures, in place whereof it would be more just that they should esteem themselves to be nought but unprofitable servants! Yet we, by custom imitating them, easily learn, together with them, to bend the word of our Teacher and Creator to our own pride. But since this word is not exactly known to us, can only be apprehended by faith, and is founded on no human reason, however specious, let us rather cast off this yoke, and investigate the mysteries of Nature, the end whereof approves the foundation of truth; and let us not only investigate these, but also the mysteries which teach us to fulfil the highest charity. And that is the treasure of the chief good which in this writing of our Archidoxies we understand in a material way.

From the aforesaid foundation we have drawn our medicine by experiment, wherein it is made clear to the eye that things are so. Then, coming to its practice, we divide this our book of Archidoxies into ten, as a sort of aid to the memory, so that we may not forget these matters, and at the same time may speak of them so far openly that we may be understood by our disciples, but not by the common people, for whom we do not wish these matters to be made too clear. We do not care to open our mind and thoughts and heart to those deaf ears, just as we do not wish to disclose them to impious men; but we shall endeavour to shut off our secrets from them by a strong wall and a key. And if by chance this our labour shall not be sufficiently safeguarded from those idiots who are enemies of all true arts, we shall forbear writing the tenth book, concerning the uses of those which precede it, so that we may not give the children's meat to the dogs. Nevertheless, the other nine will be sufficiently understood by our own disciples.

And, to speak more plainly of these matters, it must be known that in this treatise on the microcosm are proved and demonstrated all those points which it contains, which also embrace medicine, as well as those matters which are interconnected therewith. The subject of the microcosm is bound up with medicine and ruled by it, following it none otherwise than a bridled horse follows him who leads it, or a mad dog bound with chains. In this way I understand that medicine attracts Nature and everything that has life. Herein three things meet us, which show by what forces they are filled and produced. Firstly, in what way the five senses are assisted by the mysteries of Nature, though those senses do not proceed from Nature, nor spring naturally as a herb from its seed, since there is no material which produces them. Secondly, the mobility of the body is to be considered: whence it proceeds, by what power it is moved and exercised, and in what manner it is ministered to. Thirdly, there must be a knowledge of all the forces in the body, and what forces apply to each member, and are transmuted according to the same nature as the particular limb, when originally they are identical in Nature.

First, then, we will speak of these senses: sight, hearing, touch, taste, and smell. The following example teaches us. The eyes have a material substance, of which they are composed, as it is handed down in the composition of the body. So of the other senses. But vision itself does not proceed from the same source as the eye; nor the hearing from sound, or from the same source as the ears; nor touch from flesh, nor taste from the tongue, nor smell from the nostrils, any more than reason proceeds from the brain; but these are the bodily instruments, or rather the envelopes in which the senses are born. For it must not be understood that these senses depend solely on the favour of God, in the sense that they do not belong to the nature of man, but are infused solely by the grace of God above and beyond all Nature, to the end that, if one were born blind, the mighty works of God might be made known to us. We must not think so in this case. For the above-mentioned senses have each their own body, imperceptible, impalpable, just as the root of the body, on the other hand, exists in a tangible form. For man is made up of two portions, that is to say, of a material and a spiritual body. Matter gives the body, the blood, the flesh; but spirit gives hearing, sight, feeling, touch, and taste. When, therefore, a man is born deaf, this happens from a defect of the domicile in which hearing should be quartered. For the spiritual body does not complete its work in a situation which is badly disposed.

Herein, then, are recognized the mighty things of God, that there are two bodies, an eternal and a corporeal, enclosed in one, as is made clear in *Das Buch von der Gebärung* (Reading 3). Medicine acts upon the house by purging it, so that the spiritual body may be able to perfect its actions therein, like civet in a pure and uncontaminated casket.

Coming next to the power of motion in the body, let us enquire whence it is produced and has its origin, that is, how the body unites itself to the medicine so that the faculty of motion is increased. The matter is thus to be understood. Everything that lives has its own motion from Nature. This is sufficiently proved of itself so far as natural motion is concerned. But the motion of which we think may be described as that which springs from the will, as, for example, in lifting the arm one may ask how this is done, when I do not see any instrument by which I influence it; but that takes place which I desire to take place. So one must judge with leaping, walking, running, and other matters which occur in opposition to, or outside of, natural motion. They have their origin in this, that intention, a powerful mistress, exists above my notions in the following manner. The intention or imagination kindles the vegetative faculty as the fire kindles wood—as we describe more particularly in our treatise *De virtute imaginativa*. Nowhere is it more powerful to fulfil its operations than in its own body where it exists and lives. So, in every body, nothing is more easily kindled than the vegetative soul, because it runs and walks by itself and is disposed for this very purpose. For, even as a hidden or buried fire blazes forth so soon as it is exposed and catches the air, so my mind is intent upon seeing something. I cannot with my hands direct my eyes whither I will; but my imagination turns them whithersoever it is my pleasure to look. So, too, as to my motion must it be judged. If I desire to advance and arbitrarily propose this to myself, at once my body is directed to one or the other place fixed on by myself. And the more this is impressed on me by my imagination and thought, the more quickly I run. In this way, Imagination is the motive-power of my running. None otherwise does medicine purify those bodies in which there is a spiritual element, whence it happens that their motion is more easily perfected.

Thirdly, it must be understood that in the body a distribution is made over all the members of everything which is presented to it, either without or within. In this distribution a change takes place by which things are modified, so that one part subserves the constitution of the heart, another accommodates itself to the nature of the brain; and of the rest in like manner. For the body attracts to itself in two ways, from within and from without. Within, it attracts whatever is taken through the mouth. Externally, it attracts air, earth, water, and fire. Thus, then, the subject is to be arranged and defined. Those matters which are received from within need not be described. They are known by the foundation of our nature, what they are which are distributed, and we shall speak subsequently as to their division. But, externally, one must understand whatever is necessary to itself the body attracts from the four elements. Unless this were done the internal nutriment would not suffice to sustain the life of man. For instance, moisture, not existing constitutionally in the body, is extracted by the body itself from water, whence it happens that if one stands or sits in water, it is not necessary that he satisfies his thirst from without. It does not, indeed, take place in the same way that heat is extinguished by water, like fire; but the internal heat attracts to itself the moisture from without, and imbibes it just as though it were from within. Hence it happens that in the Alps cattle are able to remain the whole summer without drinking; the air is drink for them, or supplies its place: and the same should be judged with regard to man.

The nature of man, too, may be sustained in the absence of food, if the feet are planted in the earth. Thus we have seen a man who lived six months without food and was sustained only by this method: he wore a clod of earth on his stomach, and, when it got dry, took a new and fresh one. He declared that during the whole of that time he never felt hungry. The cause of this we show in the treatise *The Appetite of Nature*.

So, in the matter of medicine, we have seen a man sustain himself for many years by the quintessence of gold, taking each day scarcely half a scruple of it. In the same way, there have been many others who for so long as twenty years ate nothing, as I remember to have seen in our times. This was by some attributed to the piety and goodness of the persons themselves, or even to God, which idea we would be the last to impugn or to criticize. But this, nevertheless, is an operation of Nature; insomuch that sorrow and mental despondency take away hunger and thirst to such an extent that the body can sustain itself for many years by its own power of attraction. So, then, food and drink are not thus arranged that it is absolutely necessary we should eat bread or meats, or drink wine or water, but we are able to sustain our life on air and on clods of earth; and whatever is appointed for food, we should believe is so appointed that we should taste and try it, as we shall show more at length in *The Monarchy of God*. Let us, however, concede this point—that on account of our labours and such things, it cannot be that we do without temporal and bodily food, and that for many causes. Wherefore food was ordained for this purpose, just as medicine was against diseases.

We will make a distinction of things entering into the body after the following fashion, that they are distributed through every part of it none otherwise than as if ardent wine be poured into water. The water acquires the odour of the wine because the wine is distributed through its whole volume; and, in the same way, when ink is poured into wine the whole of the wine is thereby blackened.

So, too, in the human body, the vital moisture immediately diffuses whatever is received, and more quickly than in the examples we have cited.

But under what form the substance received becomes transmuted depends entirely on the nature of the members that receive it, just as if bread be conveyed into a man it becomes the flesh of a man, if into a fish the flesh of a fish, and so on. In the same way, it must be understood that the substances received are transmuted by the natural power of the members, and are appropriated according to the nature of the parts which take them up. A like judgement must be passed upon medicines, namely, that they are transmuted into members according to the properties of those members. For the limbs gain their own force and virtue from the substance of medicines peculiar to themselves, according to the good or bad dispersion of them, and according as the medicine itself was subtle or gross. This is the case with the quintessence; its transmutation will be stronger and more effectual. But if it be thick it remains the same, just as a picture acquires its tint, its beauty, or its deformity from its colours, and if these be more vivid it will be the same. Wherefore, in order that we may have experience of like matters to fall back upon in those things which happen to us, and that we may lay them up in our memory, so as to have them ready in case of need, we will write these nine books, keeping the tenth shut up in our own brain on account of the thankless idiots. Nevertheless, to our own disciples, these things shall be made sufficiently clear.

And let no one wonder at the school of our learning. Though it be contrary to the courses and methods of the ancients, still it is firmly based on experience, which is mistress of all things, and by which all arts should be proved.

I. iii. 93–101

5

DAS BUCH PARAGRANUM
(1529-30)

5.1

They reproach me that my writings are not like theirs; that is
the fault of their understanding, not my fault, for my writings
are well rooted in experiment and evidence and will send forth
their young shoots when the right May-time comes. They have
good cause to complain of my writings, for no one cries out
unless he is hurt; no one is hurt unless he is sensitive, unless
he is transient and impermanent. They cry out because their
art is fragile and mortal; what is not mortal does not cry out,
thus they are mortal and they cry out against me. The art of
medicine does not cry out against me, for it is immortal and
set upon such an eternal foundation that heaven and earth shall
be shattered before medicine perishes. So long as I am at peace
with medicine, why should the outcry of a mortal physician
upset me? They cry out because I wound them; it is a sign that
they themselves are sick in their medicine; this disease is their
struggle against me, because they are not pleased to be discovered and exposed.

I. viii. 53

5.2

Their worst contention against me is that I do not come out
of their schools, nor write out of their learning. If I wrote in
such a way, how should I escape punishment for lying, for the

old writings are manifestly false. What, then, can come out of them but falsehood? If I want to write the truth about their medicine, about their students, masters, and preceptors, there would have to some common ground uniting them, for they are all shouting out what medicine is, and their outcry needs to be exposed just as much as their art. So, if I attempt to write the truth about them, I must point out those bases upon which true medicine stands, in order that people may judge whether I have authority to write or not.

I. viii. 54

5.3

And because I write from the true source of medicine, I must be rejected, and you who are born neither of the true origin nor of the true heredity must adhere to the spurious art which raises itself beside the true. Who is there amongst the instructed who would not prefer what is grounded on a rock to what is grounded on sand? Only the abandoned academic drunkards who bear the name of doctor must suffer no deposition! They abide, painted doctors, and if they were not painted with this title, who would recognize them? Their works would certainly not reveal them. Outwardly they are beautiful, inwardly they are squalid dunces. What instructed and experienced man desires a doctor who is only an outward show? None. Only the simpletons desire him. What, then, is the origin of that medicine which no instructed man desires, from which no Philosophy issues, in which no Astronomy can be noted, in which no Alchemy is practised, and in which there is no vestige of Virtue? And because I point out these things essential in a physician, I must needs have my name changed by them to Cacophrastus, when I am really called Theophrastus, both for my art's sake and by my christening.

I. viii. 55

5.4

Understand then thoroughly that I am expounding the basics of medicine upon which I stand and will stand: namely, Philosophy, Astronomy, Alchemy, and Virtue. The first pillar,

Philosophy, is the knowledge of earth and water; the second pillar, Astronomy together with Astrology, has a complete knowledge of the two elements, air and fire; the third pillar, Alchemy, is knowledge of the experiment and preparation of the four elements mentioned; and the fourth pillar, Virtue, should remain with the physician until death, for this completes and preserves the other three pillars. And note well, for you too must enter here and come to understand the three pillars, otherwise it will be known by the very peasants in the villages that your trade is to treat princes and lords, towns and countries through lies and deception only and that you know neither your trade nor the truth, for the education which prepares you fits you for fools and hypocrites, all you supposed physicians. And as I take the four pillars, so must you take them too and follow after me, not I after you.

I. viii. 55-6

5.5

Follow after me, Avicenna, Galen, Rhasis, Montagnana, Mesue, etc. Follow after me, and not I after you, you from Paris, you from Montpellier, you from Swabia, you from Meissen, you from Cologne, you from Vienna and from the Danube, the Rhine, and the islands in the sea. Italy, Dalmatia, Sarmatia, Athens, Greek, Arab, Israelite, follow me and not I you. Not one of you will survive, even in the most distant corner, where even the dogs will not piss. I shall be monarch and mine will be the monarchy.

I. viii. 56

5.6

You are serpents and I expect poison from you. With what scorn have you proclaimed that I am the Luther of physicians, with the interpretation that I am a heretic. I am Theophrastus and more so than him to whom you compare me. I am that and am a monarch of physicians as well, and can prove what you are not able to prove. I will let Luther justify his own affairs, and I will account for mine, and will rise above the charges which you level against me: the arcana will raise me up to that height. Who are Luther's foes? The very rabble that hates me. And what you wish him you wish me—to the fire with us both. The heavens did not make me a physician, God made me one: it is not the business of the heavens but a gift from God. I can rejoice that rogues are my enemies, for the truth has no enemies except liars. I need wear no armour nor shield against you, for you are neither very learned nor experienced enough to refute one word of mine. I wish I could protect my bald head against the flies as efficiently as I can defend my monarchy. I will not defend my monarchy with empty talk but with arcana. And I do not take my medicines from the apothecaries, their shops are just foul sculleries which produce nothing but foul broths. But you defend yourselves with belly-crawling and flattery. How long do you think it will last? . . . Let me tell you this, the stubble on my chin knows more than you and all your scribes, my shoebuckles are more learned than your Galen and Avicenna, and my beard has more experience than all your high colleges.

I. viii. 62-5

[These polemical prefaces were followed by two books devoted to the first two pillars of medicine, Philosophy and Astronomy. It was not until the second draft of the *Paragranum*, that the complete work consisting of four books corresponding to the four pillars of medicine was completed. The work was introduced by a more moderate preface, suggesting the Paracelsus had recovered his balance after the rebuffs of Basle and Nuremberg.]

[In the book on Philosophy, there is an important passage stating the homoeopathic principle as a consequence of the 'anatomy' of the arcanum (secret remedy)]:

5.7

You should be able to recognize diseases according to their anatomy, for it is in its anatomy that the remedy is identical with the agent that caused the disease. Hence a scorpion cures scorpion poisoning, because it has the same anatomy; arsenic cures arsenic poisoning, the heart the heart, the lungs the lungs, the spleen the spleen; not ox spleen, nor is the brain of a pig any good for the brain of man, but that which corresponds to the brain in the outside world can cure the human brain. Philosophy is based on this anatomy, and from this philosopy grows the physician.

I. viii. 157

[The book on Alchemy contains another discussion of astrological medicine. In this context, astral concordance is the power of remedies which it directs to the diseased organ]:

5.8

Medicine must be understood and classified internally. You should not call a thing cold, hot, humid, or dry but should say, this is Saturn, this Mars, this Venus, this the Pole. The physician should know how to bring about a conjunction between the astral Mars and the grown Mars (i.e. the herbal remedy). In this sense the remedy should be prepared in the star and should become a star, for the stars above make us ill and die, they make us healthy . . . The physician must therefore abandon [the ancient Galenic way in the preparation of remedies based on] grades, complexions, humours, and qualities and must understand medicine in the light of the heavens, namely that there are stars both above and below. As a remedy cannot act without the heavens, it must be directed by them. Thus you must make a remedy volatile, that is to say, remove what is earthly in it, for only then will the heavens direct it. What should act in the brain will be directed to it by the Moon; what on the spleen by Saturn; what belongs to the heart will be guided to it by the Sun, and to the kidneys by Venus, by Jupiter to the liver, by Mars to the gall-bladder . . . You should not say, melissa is a herb for the womb and marjoram for the head—thus the ignorant talk. Their action lies in Venus and the Moon; if you want the herbs to be effective, the heavens must be propitious.

I. viii. 182-4

6

OPUS PARAMIRUM (1530-1)

6.1

The first thing the physician should know is that man is composed of three substances. These three form man and are man and he is them, receiving from them and in them all that is good and all that is evil for the physical body. So that the physician must know these three and must understand their combinations, their maintenance, and their analysis. For in these three lie all health and all sickness, whether whole or partial. In them therefore will be discovered the measure of health and the measure of disease: for the physician must not overlook the weight, number, and measure of disease. For according to these he can estimate the source whence it derives, and it is of great importance to understand this well before going further. Death is also due to these three, because if life be withdrawn from the primary substances in whose union life and man exist, man must die. From these primary substances therefore proceed all causes, origins, and knowledge of disease, their symptoms, development, and specific properties, and all that is essential for a physician to know.

I. ix. 40

6.2

God has so fashioned medicine that it is not consumed by fire. He has also fashioned the physician that he is born of fire. For the physician is made by medicine and not by himself; therefore he must study all Nature, and Nature is the world with all that it contains. And what Nature teaches him, that he must seek to understand. But let him seek nothing in his own knowledge, but in the light of Nature let him discover the teaching locked up in her storehouse. When the physician finds Nature open and unconcealed before him, then will the origin of health and sickness be unobscured. For since he is a physician by and from medicine and not without medicine, and since medicine is older than he, he is out of medicine and not medicine out of him. Let him search and learn from what has made him and not from himself. For the fire is in the teacher, not in the pupil.

I. ix. 41-2

6.3

There are two kinds of knowledge, that of experience and that of our own cleverness. The knowledge of experience is twofold: one kind is the foundation and teacher of the physician; the other is his misleading and error. He receives the first from the fire when he plies the Vulcanic art in transmuting, forging, reducing, solving, perfecting with all the processing pertaining to such work. And it is by such experimenting that the three substances are discovered, all that is contained in Nature, their kind, character, and properties. The other kind of knowledge is but hearsay without experiment. It may prove right once but not invariably, and it does not do to build upon such a foundation. Error is built upon it, error glossed over with sophistries. . . For we cannot be taught medicine by hearsay or by reading, but by learning. Nature in the fire of experiment shall be our teacher. . . We can no longer believe in the four humours existing in man; it is but a matter of belief. But medicine does not belong to faith, but to the evidence of our eyes. Nothing but the sickness and health of the soul is a matter of faith. All bodily medicine is a visible matter and requires no faith. . . Hence, the physician must be called to the profession. Medicine grows out of the earth for him. The earth knows him, establishes and rejects him. The reason why we can recognize and experience the three substances does not lie in our

minds nor in hearsay but in the experiencing of Nature, its analysis, and the establishment of its properties—for man is taught
by the Great World and not by man. It is the concordance which
makes man whole, from which he derives knowledge of the
world and hence of himself—which are a unity and not two
things. I put this to the test of experience.

I. ix. 43-5

6.4

There are three substances which give every single thing its
body. The names of these three things are Sulphur, Mercury,
and Salt. These three are combined to make a body and nothing else is added save life and that which pertains to it. If you
take an object in your hand, you have these three substances
concealed within one body. A peasant can tell you that you
are holding a piece of wood, but you also know that you have
a compound of Sulphur, Mercury, and Salt. If you have a bone
and can say whether it is mostly Sulphur, Mercury, or Salt,
you know why it is diseased or what is the matter with it. The
peasant can see the externals, but the physician's task is to see
the inner and secret matter. In order to make these things visible, Nature must be compelled to show itself. . . Take a piece
of wood. It is a body. Now burn it. The flammable part is the
Sulphur, the smoke is the Mercury, and the ash is the Salt. The
peasant cannot understand the process of combustion, but the
physician can with the eyes of medicine.

I. ix. 45-6

6.5

What is the taste other than a need in the anatomy in which
nothing is important except to reach its own like? It follows
that as this *gustus* [taste] is distributed to every member in the
body, each desires its own like, the sweet desires the sweet, the
bitter desires the bitter, each in its degree and measure, as those
held by the plants sweet, sour, and bitter. Shall the liver seek
medicine in gentian, agaric, or colocynth? No. Shall the gall-
bladder seek medicine in manna, honey, sugar, or the polyp-
ody fern? No, for like seeks its like. Nor in the order of anat-

omy shall cold be a cure for heat, nor heat for cold. It would be a wild disorder if we were to seek our cure in contraries. A child asks his father for bread and he does not give him a snake. God has created us and he gives us what we ask, not snakes. So it would be bad medicine to give bitters where sugar is required. The gall-bladder must have what it asks, and the heart too, and the liver. It is a fundamental pillar upon which the physician should rest to give to each part of the anatomy the special thing that accords with it. For the bread which the child eats has an anatomy similar to his own, and the child eats as it were his own body. Therefore each sickness in the anatomy must have its own corresponding medicine. He who does not understand the anatomy finds it difficult to act if he be honest and simple; but it is worse with those whose honour is small and whom shame and crime do not trouble. They are the enemies of the light of Nature. . . What blind man asks for bread from God and receives poison? If you are experienced and grounded in anatomy you will not give stones instead of bread. For know that you are the father rather than the physician of your patients: therefore feed them as a father does his child. As a father must support his child according to his need and must give him the food which becomes himself, so must the physician care for his patients.

I. ix. 63-4

6.6

Christ who is the Truth has given us no false remedy but one that is compatible and arcane. For far be it from us to say that Christ knew not the simplicia of Nature. Therefore oil and wine must be competent, else there is no foundation in medicine. . . Let it be manifest to you that a grain of wheat yields no fruit unless it be cast into the ground and die there. Thus the wound is the earth, and the oil and wine the grain. You must guess what the fruit is.

I. ix. 65-6

6.7

There are three anatomies which should be maintained in man:

first *localis*, which tells us form, propositions, substance of a man and all that pertains to him; the second shows the living Sulphur, the flowing Mercury, the sharp Salt in each organ; and the third instructs us what kind of anatomy death brings, that is *mortis anatomia*, and in what manner and likeness he comes. For the light of Nature shows that death comes in as many forms as there are species from the elements; there are as many kinds of death as there are kinds of corruption. And just as each corruption gives birth to another, it requires anatomy. It comes in many forms until one after another we all die and are consumed through corruption. But beyond all these anatomies, there is also a uniform science in the anatomy of medicine, and beyond them all stand heaven, earth, water, and air, and the heavens and all the stars have their part in the new anatomy. For Saturn must give his *saturnum*, Mars his *martem*, and until these are discovered, the art of medicine has not been found. For as the tree grows out of the seed, so must all that seems now invisible grow into new life, for it is there, and it must come to pass that it shall be visible. For the light of Nature is a light to make men see and it is neither dark nor dim. And it must come to pass that we shall use our eyes in that light to see those things that we require to see. They will not be otherwise than they are now; but we must be otherwise able to see them. We must see in a different manner to the peasant. The light of Nature must kindle our eyes.

I. ix. 68-9

6.8

All our nourishment becomes ourselves; we eat ourselves into being. So also in medicine, with this difference, that the treatment must match the disease. In health all that is worn out is restored to each organ by and in itself. Do not be astonished at this: a tree which stands in the field would not be a tree, had it no nourishment. What is nourishment? It is not a mere feeding or stuffing, but the restoration of form. What is hunger? It is a precursor of future death in the waste of the organs. For the form is carved by God himself in the womb. This carving abides in the form of each type, but it wastes and dies without addition from without. He who does not eat does not grow, he who does not eat does not last. Therefore he who grows, grows by nourishment, and the shaper is with him to give form, and without it he cannot exist. Whence it follows that the nourishment of each carven type has the form within itself in which it grows and develops. Rain has the tree in itself, and so has the earth sap. Rain is the drink, earth sap the food, by which the tree grows. What is it that grows? What the tree absorbs from rain and earth sap becomes wood and bark. The shaper is in the seed, wood and bark are in the earth sap and the rain. The craftsman in the seed can make wood out of these two things. And it is the same with plants; the seed is nothing but a beginning in which is the form and the craftsman, the type and property. If it is to germinate, the rain, dew, and earth sap must develop the plant, for in these are the stalks, leaves, flowers, and so on.

I. ix. 71–2

6.9

There must therefore be an outward form in all nourishment for growth, and if we do not receive it, we never grow but die in the neglected form. And if we are grown up, we must preserve our form, lest it waste away. For we have in us what resembles fire, which consumes our form. If we did not supply and support the form of our body, it would die neglected. Therefore what we eat becomes ourselves so that we do not die through the decay of our form. In this way we eat our fingers, our body, blood, flesh, feet, brain, heart, and so on. For every bite we take contains in itself all our organs, all that is included in the whole man, all of which he is constituted . . . When summer is at hand, the trees become hungry because they want to put forth leaves, blossom, fruit. They have not got these within themselves, otherwise trees that were cut down would put forth leaves as well as those still standing. They stand in the earth whence they receive these things into their own form, where the craftsmen shapes them according to the kind of each; that is his contribution. Know therefore that in order

to preserve their form and type from being consumed, all living things become hungry and thirsty.

I. ix. 72-3

6.10

There are two men, visible and invisible. That which is visible
is twofold, namely, like the body in this example. An image
is carved out of wood, in which it could not be originally discerned. This is the nourishment, which once in the body goes
into all its organs. It does not remain in one part, but is richly
used. For the great Artist carves it, He who makes man, and
distributes to the organs so as to make man. Now we know
that we eat ourselves; every tree and every creature that lives,
and we must now learn further what follows from this concerning medicine. We do not eat bone, blood vessels, ligaments,
and seldom brain, heart, and entrails, nor fat; therefore bone
does not make bone, nor brain brain, but every bite contains
all these. Bread is blood, but who sees it? It is fat, who sees
it? For the master-craftsman in the stomach is good. He can
make iron out of brimstone; he is there daily and shapes the
man according to his form. He can make diamonds out of salt,
and gold out of mercury. He is more concerned with man than
with things, so he labours at him in all that is necessary. Bring
him the material, let him divide it and shape it as it should be,
for he knows the measure, number, weight, proportion, length
and all. Know then that every creature is twofold, one out of
the seed, the other out of nourishment... He has death within
himself, and through nourishment he must hold it at bay.

I. ix. 73-4

6.11

The body is developed from Sulphur, that is, the whole body
is one Sulphur, and that a subtle Sulphur which burns and destroys invisibly. Blood is one Sulphur, flesh is another, the major
organs another, the marrow another, and so on; and this Sulphur is volatile. But the different bones are also Sulphur, only
their Sulphur is fixed: in scientific analysis each Sulphur can
be distinguished. Now the stiffening of the body comes from

Salt: without the Salt no part of the body could be grasped. From Salt the diamond receives its hard texture, iron its hardness, lead its soft texture, alabaster its softness, and so on. All stiffening or coagulation comes from Salt. There is therefore one Salt in the bones, another in the blood, another in the flesh, another in the brain, and so on. For as many as there are Sulphurs there are also Salts. The third substance of the body is Mercury, which is a fluid. All parts of the body have their own fluid: thus the blood has one, the flesh has another, the bones, the marrow, each has its own fluid, which is Mercury. So that Mercury has as many forms as Sulphur and Salt. But since man must have a complete form, its various parts must compact, stiffen, and have a fluid: the three form and unite one body. It is one body but of three substances. Sulphur burns, it is only a sulphur; Salt is an alkali, for it is fixed; Mercury is a vapour, for it does not burn but evaporates. Know then that all dissolution arises from these three.

I. ix. 82-3

6.12

The three substances are in the four elements, or mothers of all things; for out of the elements proceed all things: from earth come plants, trees, and all their varieties; from water, metals, stones, and all minerals; from the air, dew and manna; from fire, thunder, rays of light, snow, and rain. And when the microcosm is broken up, part becomes earth, and so wonderful that in a brief time it bears the fruits whose seed has been sown therein, and this the physician should know. Out of the broken body, too, comes the second element, water; and as water is the mother of the minerals, the alchemist can compound rubies out of it. And the dissolution also gives the third element, fire, from which hail can be drawn. And air too ascends from the rising spirit, just as dew forms inside a closed glass. Many have begun to treat of this generation of creation, but they have failed. There is another transmutation after these, and it yields every kind of Sulphur, Salt, and Mercury which the microcosmic world can demonstrate. This is very important, for it concerns man's quest for health, his water of life, his Philosopher's Stone, his arcanum, his balsam, his golden drink, and the like. All these things are in the microcosm; just as they are in the outer world, they are in the inner world.

I. ix. 91-2

6.13

Therefore man is his own physician; for as he helps Nature she gives him what he needs, and gives him his herbal garden according to the requirements of his anatomy. If we consider and observe all things funamentally we discover that in ourselves is our physician and in our own nature are all things that we need. Take our wounds: what is needed for the healing of wounds? Nothing except that the flesh should grow from within outwards, not from the outside inwards. Therefore the treatment of wounds is a defensive treatment, that no contingency from without may hinder our nature in its working. In this way our nature heals itself and levels and fills up itself, as surgery teaches the experienced surgeon. For the *mumia* is the man himself, the *mumia* is the balsam which heals the wound: mastic, gums, glaze will not give a morsel of flesh; but they can protect the working of Nature so as to assist it.

I. ix. 92-3

6.14

Since man derives from the *limbus* and the *limbus* is the whole world, it follows that each several thing finds its like in the other. For were man not made out of the whole in every part of the whole, he could not be the microcosm, nor would he be capable of attracting to himself all that is the macrocosm. But as he is made out of the whole, all that he eats out of the Great World is part of himself: for he must be maintained by that of which he is made. For as a son is born from his father and no one helps the son so naturally as the father, in the same way the curative members of the outer world help the members of the inner world. For the Great World has all the human proportions, divisions, parts, members just as man has; and man receives these in food and medicine. These parts are separated one from another for the sake of the whole and its form. In

science their general body is the *physicum corpus*. So man's body
receives the body of the world, as a son his father's blood; for
these are one blood and one body, separated only by the soul,
but in science without separation. It follows then that heaven
and earth, air and water are a man in science, and man is a world
with heaven and earth, air and water in science. So the Saturn
of the microcosm receives from Saturn in the heavens, as the
Jupiter of the heavens takes from the Jupiter of the microcosm.
The melissa of the earth takes from the melissa of the microcosm . . . and they are all in union. Therefore heaven and earth,
air and water are one substance, not four, nor two, nor three,
but one. Where they are not in union, the substance has been
destroyed or broken up.

I. ix. 94-5

6.15

We must therefore understand that when we administer medicine, we administer the whole world: that is, all the virtue of
heaven and earth, air and water. Because if there is sickness in
the body, all the healthy organs must fight against it, not only
one, but all. For one sickness can be death to them all: note
how Nature struggles against sickness with all her power.
Therefore your medicine must contain the whole firmament
of both upper and lower spheres. Think with what energy
Nature strives against death when she takes heaven and earth
with all their powers to help her. So too must the soul fight
against the devil with all her might . . . Nature has a horror
of cruel and bitter death, which our eyes cannot see, nor our
hands clutch. But Nature sees and knows and clutches him:
therefore she employs the powers of heaven and earth against
the terrible one, for terrible he is and monstrous, hideous, and
harsh. As he who made him, Christ on the Mount of Olives,
who sweated blood and prayed to his Father to take him
away—it is reasonable that Nature should be appalled. For the
better death is known, the greater is the value of medicine, a
refuge which the wise seek.

I. ix. 95-6

6.16

One may derive from this the various kinds of Mercury-diseases: in one it affects the reason, in another the blood vessels, in another the tongue, and so on. It begins with a heat that inflames the body, and where this is most acute the process will occur, as if that place were an oven in which there lay Mercury. In severe cases, the whole body is convulsed and all its limbs are in fever. It can occur that the Mercury rises and falls as in the process of distillation, then it does its worst and death is near. As already stated there are three ways. The distillation of Mercury causes a swift death; the second, the precipitation of Mercury, causes podagra [gout], chiragra, and arthritis; the third, the sublimation of Mercury, causes mania and brain fever. Mercury is so subtle that it can permeate the bones and flesh, causing pustules, gall trouble, syphilis, leprosy, and such like, and in the rising of the heat it brings about shivering, cold sweats, and shaking . . .

I. ix. 102-4

6.17

Just as Mercury can be produced, so Salt as another of the three substances can cause diseases. Salt is subject to four processes: resolution, calcination, reverberation, and alkalification, which all occur in the body as in the outside world. Thus too much Salt goes into solution in people who indulge in overeating or lechery. In these, Salt is converted into fat. Obese bodies are like land which has been over-manured, it brings fruit too quickly on, or like land which as suffered an excess of rain, causing the fruit to decay . . . Salt is calcined when fluid is withdrawn and alum is formed. This causes perspiration, itching skin, later on scabs and sores . . . When it is reverberated, it goes up and down as though distilled. Vital spirit blown upon its surface makes it mucilaginous and sticky, and in this form it is driven by the fever to the surface of the body, when it appears in the form of rusty wounds called *vulnera aeruginosa*. Any external disease, notably ulcers, cancers, baldness, pustulae, scars, condylometa, morphea, and leprosy, are Salt-diseases,

varying according to the type of Salt. For it is Salt which gives
form to all things.

I. ix. 105-8

6.18

It is the four elements which can break down and transform
Sulphur. They are the artists which transmute Sulphur and cause
it to generate disease in four types, cold, hot, moist, and dry.
Know then that each element contains some coldness within
it, but coldness is the element earth. Coldness can be either
hard or moist. Hardness is twofold; congealed or frozen, coagulated or fluid; moistness is twofold; dissolved or melted,
resolved or decomposed. A fiery coldness causes congealment,
like frozen water, snow, fine gravel, and so on. Thus a congealment in Sulphur can be likened to those diseases having
a similarity to snow, frost, and gravel. The coagulation of coldness derives from the element water and is solid, while conge-
lation is volatile. Examples of the coagulation are coral, alum,
entalia, and aluminium salts, and diseases which come from
coagulated coldness, the coldness of water, have a similar form.
A coldness also comes from the air, neither congealed nor
coagulated but a wind, so that such wind colds, chaos colds,
and air colds can be found in the body. These diseases also
resemble the cold plants, solatrum, rosa, lactuca, portulaca, and
so on . . . There is also an element fire in the earth which
inflames Sulphur. You can see hare's foot and nettle growing
in the earth, and thus you can recognize these energies when
present in the physical body . . . You also have a moistness from
the four elements . . . and it is the same with dryness . . . Thus
there are four species of this kind of disease, and they can be
reasonably understood in these categories.

I. ix. 108-12

6.19

There are influences which cause sweating, purgation, heat, and
the like, and which must be reckoned with, for they are specific
maladies: they do not spring from visible causes, but are innate
and of such a nature that one man has a tendency to sweat,

another to purgation, another to this, another to that. For know that from the spermata far more births are present than actually take place. The camphor and other plants demonstrate that, and this is the cause of diseases in the bladder and kidneys. Such too is tartar which forms stone. What is hereditary we cannot eradicate; for the seed must produce all that is dormant within it. But it is not necessarily hereditary to be born blind; and although a man may be born blind, sight may be in him although not properly developed. If a man has six fingers on one hand and four on the other, or they are not in their right places, nothing can be done for him, because the defect is in the substance of the body. But no experienced physician can say that the blind man may not be helped, for Nature is great and wonderful, and if sight is within him it may be produced, for sight is a wind which has no body and it may be guided to its own place, which cannot be done in the case of the deformed body. Innate things are like the hardness of iron and the colour of chalk and must be accepted as they come. For we cannot prevent snow from falling, but we can prevent it from doing harm to men.

I. ix. 113-14

6.20

Just so is the sperm of man which is *limbus* and in the four elements. Know now that it has such a power; these powers are best called influences, for they are influences. But it is an astronomical error when men say that an influence comes from the stars. The heavens send no influences. We receive our form from the hand of God. Whatever we may be, God has made us and carved all our organs. Our conditions, properties, habits, we receive from the inbreathing of life wherewith these things are given to us. What diseases we have come to us from three substances, as already described, which have something to impress on us, as fire in wood or straw, or saffron on water. That is the influence which we cannot drive away from us, as we can drive away the maladies originating from the *limbus* outside us. Thus it is an impression from the sperm and we cannot drive it away. Men speak of an *inclinatio*: it is nonsense. They say man receives an *inclinatio* from Mars, Saturn, the Moon, and so on. This is error and deception. It would be more reasonable to say 'Mars imitates man', for man is greater than Mars or the other planets. He who knows the heavens and understands men says nothing. He might say: 'Man is so noble in God's eyes and so highly accounted that his image is counterfeited in the heavens with all that he does and leaves undone, his good and his evil.' But that is not *inclinatio*. The relationship between heaven and man is twofold: the first that his image is counterfeited in heaven; the second is the prelude, in that all men's future work, mode of life, and behaviour is represented in advance, but in the form of a prophecy rather than a cause.

I. ix. 114-16

6.21

As we find written in the Scriptures, we must rise on the last day in our body and give account of our misdeeds. The body which is nothing in our eyes has sinned and must rise again with us. For we shall not give an account of our diseases nor of our health and the like, but of the things which proceed from the heart, for these concern man, and these too are a body, not out of the *limbus* but from the breath of God. But since we shall in our flesh see God our Saviour, it must be that the body made of the *limbus*, which is our body of flesh, shall be there too. Who would wish to be ignorant of those things revealed through the mouth of God? We shall rise again in the flesh, in the body made from the *limbus*, which has its own measure and uses, and what exceeds that comes from the intangible body which transcends the bounds of Nature.

I. ix. 117-18

6.22

All that is growing and living must eat, and thus they need a stomach and the virtue of digestion. Now food has constituents pure and impure; the good thing is separated from the bad and is used to nourish the organism the bad thing cannot be assimilated by the anatomy of the organism, but retains its own anatomy. Yet it remains in that organism. Thus the organism contains *stercus* [refuse] as well as nourishment. It is this *stercus* which matters here . . . Now the human stomach, the first stomach which is suspended from the neck-tube, can but achieve the first digestion, separating the good things from the *stercus*, which it then delegates to the subtle stomach which is in the mesenteric vessels, in the liver, kidneys, bladder, and gut. Thus there are refuse materials in the body which are neither faeces in the ordinary sense nor subject to incorporation in man. They cannot be broken down, yet they are not man and they remain in man. Now there are such diseases which are caused by this refuse and vary according to the degree of separation and the location of the refuse. These diseases are stone and sand, glue and mud. Now tell me how your humours could become stone, sand, mud, and glue without being so originally. These four are four types of refuse from food. They are all known as tartar.

I. ix. 123–5

6.23

One should know how we ingest tartar. It is in the vegetables like barley and peas which you can deduce from the mucus they produce and their thick texture. All kinds of food with this mucus lead to stone in the body. Milk products, meat, and fish have sand in them and this becomes tartar. In the same way we have two kinds of excrement in drink, wine and water. But one should note that fruit juices like pear and apple juice may be compared with wine and water. But beer has two kinds of tartar in it, those of vegetables and the water from which it is made. There is a mitigating factor in these drinks, in so far as they pass quickly through the body, and the less they are digested, the better it is. Because a strong digestion quickly produces stone or tartar, it is better to have a weak digestion. A weak digestion never produces stone or tartar, but an ardent strong one is so quick and thorough, that it lets nothing through. That is why one man may have tartar, the other none . . . Know too that the two kinds of tartar in drink vary according to the nature and property of countries . . . Thus it may happen that a Swiss suffers from a Nuremberg or Westenburg tartar owing to the consumption of cereals and vegetables imported from those places.

I. ix. 128-30

6.24

How does tartar finally develop in the lungs, gall-bladder, heart, spleen, brain, and kidneys? Each of these organs must eat and take its daily nourishment from the stomach. Each organ in the body acts as its own stomach and separates out what is not good for it, and no organ performs this separation or 'cooking' for another one, save the stomach, which does so on behalf of the liver, kidneys and bladder, that is on behalf of the whole community of organs. But this communal function is not sufficient, so that each organ must perform the process and thereby achieve its own specific nutrition. Whatever such an organ rejects is excrement and must be disposed of by many kinds of exits, the lungs coughing it up, the brain emitting it through the nose, the spleen through the blood vessels, the bile through the stomach, the kidneys through the bladder, the heart into a chaos . . . The tartar in these organs is not visible, because it is volatile and goes into these organs like a brandy that evaporates and appears to be devoid of body. It is there, however, and even if it is placed in a still and circulates, it still has the tartar in itself.

I. ix. 147-8

6.25

If one reckons how much a man eats and then subtracts the refuse and urine, only a small part can remain in the body. That is why only a small amount of tartar can be found in the individual organs besides the pathways of the urine and the gut . . . This applies to the tartar in the lungs, which appears in men and beasts as small stones resembling wheat or millet seeds. The bronchial tubes are the stomach of the lungs, in which it separates the pure from the impure. Hence there is a specific lung excrement in the air tubes, in which it is distilled, and from which it should be coughed up. If it is not, but remains there, it is transformed into fine leaves, slate particles, and granules and obstructs the air tubes, preventing their free movement up and down in respiration and causing many kinds of disease. These are called asthma, coughing, phthisis, and hectic fever, yet they all derive from tartar in the lungs.

I. ix. 149-51

6.26

The stomach of the brain lies outside it in the upper interior parts of the nose, and it is through the latter that brain excrement is voided. It is here in the brain's stomach that tartar is found, causing insanity, mania, and similar disorders, commonly and erroneously attributed to the blood . . . You should know more about the kidneys. Although the urine is in the kidneys, they do not nourish themselves from it, but take another food in common with the other organs . . . Thus the kidneys also have their particular excrement which is contained in the urine and is excreted with it and is the hypostasis (deposit). Hence the deposit gives a verdict on kidney problems . . . There is an art in the separation of the deposit from the urine, and whoever can do it, can see the excrement of the kidneys clearly and therein the stones.

I. ix. 152-3

6.27

Now it is necessary to discuss the same processes in the outer world. The same kind of stones derive from the waters of the elements which are productive of stone. They rise up in the form of dew and end up in heaven as the *primae materiae* of the stones. The still world harbours in itself the generation of these strange things—invisible to philosophy—but visible in their ultimate result. Now when the products of Salt prevail in heaven and encounter this dew, meteorites are formed which fall to earth until the heaven is empty. These astra and elements are in the body as they are in heaven. All men are heavens, made from one *limbus*. It therefore follows that a stone is suddenly produced in man, each time that a body is produced in heaven . . . Now original matter in man is all spirits and all stars and is subject to the same course of time. So you shall know that

he who has the same astrally predestined course will not escape
the stone.

I. ix. 171-2

6.28

Now there are three kinds of matrix: the first is the water on
which the spirit of the Lord was borne, and this was the matrix
in which heaven and earth were created. Then heaven and earth
became a matrix, in which Adam was formed by the hand of
God. Then woman was created out of man; she is the matrix
of all men until the end of the world. What did the first matrix
contain within itself? As the kingdom of God it encompassed
the spirit of God. The world encloses the eternal, by which
it is itself surrounded. Woman is enclosed in her own skin, and
everything within it forms the matrix. Thus her body cannot
be compared with that of man, although she was taken from
him. It is true that she resembles him, for she has received his
image, but in all other things, in essence, properties, nature,
and peculiarities, she is quite different from him. For man suffers
as man, woman suffers as woman, both suffer as two creatures
beloved of God. He proves this with the twofold medicine
which he gives us: a masculine medicine for men, a feminine
medicine for women.

I. ix. 192-3

6.29

God created man from the matrix without any aid or other
agency. He took him from the matrix and made a man of him.
Moreover this was never repeated, as He gave the *limbus* to man
in his natural being, so that he might be the *limbus*, that is
become his own son. And when he wants to have the son, He
gave him a matrix of his own, namely woman. Henceforth there
will be progeny from two, not from man, nor from the mother
by herself, but from man in the matrix. To that end there will
be two, and yet only one; two kinds of flesh, yet only one, not
two. This means that both make man, neither can alone. Thus
they are two in one, and yet they are only one, although two.
Thus is man created from the *limbus*, which is the father, but

he is shaped, built, and endowed in the matrix, just as the first man was created in the macrocosm, the Great World.

I. ix. 193-4

6.30

What causes the sea to rise? Just as the sea expels things and falls, one may understand woman as a mother of children. The sea is the mother of water. Because woman is a mother, she produces such rivers in herself, which rise up and flow out every four weeks . . . Thus the menstrual blood is an excrement of things flowing into the matrix, which die there and are then expelled. Some doctors have mistakenly called the menstrual blood a blossom of women. Women blossom at the moment of conception, and the fruit—that is the child—follows as in the case of all blossoms . . . When a tree blossoms, it is always because of the fruit that desires to ripen in it, and the tree in which no fruit lies hidden does not blossom. According to the erroneous analogy, a virgin may blossom, but she has no fruit in her . . . Do you not realize that the matrix is nothing but the microcosm?! If it is to give birth, then it must be pure . . . thus she remains pure until the milk ceases. As long as pregnancy lasts, there is no excrement, for all things are quiet and bide their time . . . For this is the nature of woman, that she is transformed as soon as she conceives; and then all things in her are like a summer, there is no snow, no frost, and no winter, but only pleasure and delight.

I. ix. 196-8

6.31

A woman is like a tree bearing fruit. And man is like the fruit that the tree bears. The tree must be well nourished until it has everything that it needs in order to give, which is why it is there. But consider how much injury the tree can bear and how much less the pears. By that much woman is also superior to man. Man is to her what the pear is to the tree. The pear falls but the tree remains standing. The tree continues to care for further fruit in the course of its long life, therefore it must also receive much, suffer much, bear up with much for the sake

of its fruits, in order that they may thrive well and happily . . .
Thus you must note what is wrong with the tree but not wrong
with the pears, and what is wrong with the pears but not wrong
with the tree. And similarly in the case of women and men.
The difference between little boys and little girls is similar to
that difference between pears and their pips.

I. ix. 200-1

6.32

Thus is the microcosm, that is the matrix or the Little World,
and it contains within itself all the minerals. It follows that the
body can take its medicine from the world and thus it also follows that all minerals may have some benefit for man, each one
according to the mineral in the microcosm or body. These
things are revealed by philosophy, on which medicine is based.
When the physician says that marcasite [bismuth] is good for
this, then he must know beforehand that marcasite is in the
world and that it is in the human microcosm. This is how the
philosopher speaks. If he wants to speak as a physician, however,
he must say, this marcasite is the man's disease, hence it will
cure him. A hole rotting in the skin and eating into the body,
what else is it but a mineral? Then follows: colcothar mends
the hole. Why? Because colcothar is the salt that makes the hole.
Thus Mercury cures the holes which it has provoked and other
Arsenicals do likewise.

I. ix. 210-11

6.33

How marvellously man is made and formed, if one only knows
how to penetrate into his true nature, understand what he is,
and work out all his details. And it is a great thing, which you
should consider: there is nothing in heaven or in earth that is
not also in man. For these are the heavenly powers which work
in him. For God, who is in heaven, is in man. Where else can
heaven be if not in man? As we need it, it must be within us.
Therefore it knows our prayer even before we have uttered it,
for it is closer to our hearts than to our words. God made his
heaven in man great and beautiful, noble and good. For God

is in his heaven, that is in man, for He tells us Himself that
He is in us and that we are His temple. Therefore one should
watch the physician well, for he has the noblest and greatest
being in his hands.

I. ix. 219-20

6.34

We must describe the other half of man, in order that the physician may understand him as a whole. Although this aspect
is invisible, it may be seen in the light of Nature ... We men
on earth, what do we know about phenomena without the light
of Nature? It is the light of Nature that makes invisible things
visible. Whatever the eyes can see requires little proof, but much
proof is necessary to adduce something invisible as visible. You
should know that the world and all we see in it is but a half
part of the world, and the part which we do not see is just as
much involved in its motion, nature, and properties. And there
is a half part of man in which the invisible world is effective
and finds its counterpart. Thus these two worlds make two
men in one body. Creatures are so wonderful that they can be
investigated in the light of Nature, both in what God has made
invisible in them and in that which we can see. Thus God applies
his magnalia, that is works, and thus is the school of the light
of Nature, that we should not only satisfy our eyes but wonder
and investigate the phenomena which we cannot see and yet
which confront us as clearly as a pillar stands before a blind
man ... Consider this example: one cannot see colours in
moonlight but one can see them clearly in sunlight. The light
of Nature similarly surpasses the light of the sun ... it surpasses all the powers of sight.

I. ix. 252-3

6.35

It is the same when we hear a bell on a dark night; we cannot
see it and yet we do see the work of the bell, that is we hear
it. If we wish to see what is making the sound, that must happen by means of a light. Such a light is the moon, but it is wan;
the sun shines more brightly. Thus we may not content our-

selves with the light which happens to shine on the works and makes them visible, but rather we must search further and consider that the cause of the work is more than the work, and will thus require more light. For every work has a light in which it can be seen, and every light makes visible its own province, which would seem invisible in another light ... A study of works leads us to their cause ... Dionysius the Areopagite understood astrology but he could not understand the meaning of Christ on the Cross in its light; he did not want to be drowned [overwhelmed] by the work, but he wanted to understand the Creator, so he sought another light and found it. For whoever seeks and knocks, he shall find. So we will find diseases, whose origin cannot be understood in the visible body, which exhort us not to say 'it is beyond my understanding', but to kindle the light in order that we can say, 'it within our understanding'.

I. ix. 253-5

6.36

That is why I wanted to warn you, reader, to understand clearly all the following diseases, because just as all works are visible, so too must be their causes. And do not be downcast that all things are not as clear as day, but consider how secretive God is. And when we learn something, we discover that we erroneously called the invisible things invisible, for all works teach us that they have a cause. Likewise a house is a work and is visible, the master-craftsman is a work of God and the house is the work of the master-craftsman. It should be understood that we see the works visibly before our eyes, and once we have investigated its author, that is also visible to us. In matters eternal it is belief that makes all things visible, in matters corporeal it is the light of Nature that reveals all things invisible.

I. ix. 257

6.37

It behoves me to write about natural phenomena, and once they have been described, many things which were previously secret and not properly understood will be understood. For just as the physician can prepare the fifth essence of gold and discredit Avicenna the Sophist and the writings of his followers, so too can a swindler in medicine say, 'Nature does not do it, Asmodeus does it', and he could well assert it and give proof, because the sophisticated physicians would defer to him out of ignorance. Who is so daring as to guess at all Nature's powers? For these powers all proceed from divine wisdom, but who can fathom all this wisdom, when the Scriptures say that it is boundless and talk of its great profundity and mystery? What is man upon earth, what is he in his works and thoughts, when he contemplates the highest peaks in the light of Nature? Nothing, for not even if he were above the sun, or indeed above the new sun which is seven times brighter, not even here has divine wisdom begun. Because the light of Nature is like the crumbs from the table of the Lord, for all the heathen to grasp, and has departed from Judah, it behoves us not to give in, but to pick up the crumbs as long as they fall.

I. ix. 306-7

6.38

Each thing to be explained in the light of Nature must be related to the first Creation. For each beginning is the origin, property, and nature of its successor, since like does not beget unlike. The first Creation is heaven and earth, not only in their form and shape but in their natural powers and properties and man was made by the hand of God in His image from all these things following their creation . . . So man is the Little World in form, bodily substance, and all powers and virtues corresponding to the Great World. Man thus bears the noble name 'microcosm' in the sense that all heavenly orbits, terrestrial nature, watery properties, and airy essence inhere in him. The nature of all fruits of the earth and all mineral ores of water, all the constellations, and the four winds of the world are in him. What is there upon earth whose nature and power does not reside in man? God formed man according to His image from the *limbus* which has no like in nobility, subtlety, and strength . . . These great wonderful things are all in man, all powers of the herbs and trees are found in the *mumia*, not just the powers of the earth, but also those of water, all the properties of the metals, all the nature of the marcasites, all the essence of precious stones. They are all in man.

I. ix. 308-9

6.39

Whoever could separate and analyse the constituents of man would find all that he desired. Melissa is there, antimony too, all things are in this *mumia*, and these things are all natural, only not previously recognized. Thus it behoves one to speak of microcosmic powers and explain these invisible influences, which the common folk express in terms of sorcery, witch-craft and Satanism, because they are all natural and have natural causes. For you must recognize a twofold nature in the human body: a tangible virtue and an intangible virtue; for both the visible body and the invisible body have their natural influences.

I. ix. 309-10

6.40

If one was to regard such events as Christ's resurrection [and the wonders of the Saints] as natural phenomena and signs, then Christ's words 'there will be great signs' would be confirmed. But ignorance caused man to see these events as supernatural, just as the first practitioners of medicine were revered as gods by the common folk. The same thing occurs in the case of these bodies [of Christ and the Saints] because one did not know that virtues inhered in them. The unglorified body is nothing but a natural object. Coloquinth purges and all arcana for that matter act in heathens as well as Christians. Nature is simply following its own inherent order and command.

I. ix. 319

6.41

Things are innate in us . . . Whenever special virtues are born in the world, they remain in the body after death. Although the spirit has departed, the innate nature and properties of the body remain there lying in the earth, like saffron in a tin, and the earth is as well-endowed with such bodies as an apothecary is with tins of herbs. And if Christ had not talked of such signs, who would be so bold as to search so thoroughly for them in Nature? Who would not grasp the hub of Nature from whence these signs come?

I. ix. 323–4

6.42

The natural virtues are so much better than Hippocrates, who could not accomplish anything without the power of suggestion. They heal invisibly and there is no difference other than suggestion and non-suggestion. But medicine is not what the teeth chew; no one can see medicine. Because no one can see it, the body of medicine is of no account . . . If Death can creep in and throttle and kill us, so too can medicine. It is not a matter of body but of virtues, which is why the fifth essence was invented, of which one loth [half an ounce] is superior to the twenty pounds of the body from which it was extracted. The less body, the higher the value of the virtues. Just as the sun can shine through a glass and fire act through the walls of a stove, so bodies can send out invisible forces over distances while remaining at rest themselves.

I. ix. 325

7

LABYRINTHUS MEDICORUM ERRANTIUM (1538)

7.1

For man is the *corpus physicum* and the elements are the *corpus limus*, and the *corpus physicum* derives from the *corpus limus*. Thus the body retains the essence of the *limus*, just as a son retains his father's essence in his flesh and blood. Know therefore that the elements of physical bodies are . . . mothers [matrices], and from them grow good and evil, health and disease, purity and impurity, thorns and roses, gold and talcum, hail and dew, manna and mist, and the same things erupt in man, who incorporates the same virtue of the thistles and the lilies, quicksilver and gold pigment, and all creations proceed from him. These are the diseases of man, and the physician must know all such procreations. And he must know the *corpus limus* rather than the *corpus physicum* in the first instance, understand its letters, so that he may make a whole word and then a sentence . . . and thereby understand that the *corpus limus* precedes the *corpus physicum*.

I. xi. 179

7.2

Now it also follows that the physician should know how there are many species of bodies in a single physical body . . . and how all the elements are constituted therein . . . Accordingly, he must also find such a monarchy of the world in man . . .

He should know equally well by heart how many species of wood, stones, and herbs there are and that these very species are present in man, though not in their elemental form, but in the form of health or disease. Gold is the same in the elements as in man, that is a tonic. And you should know that all the other species of the elements are also in the microcosm. Whoever can take a species and recognize it in the physical body by saying that is sapphire in man, that is mercury, that is cypress, that is gold essence, has understood the book of the physical body well. And thereupon he is a physician and finds his theory, which is not merely speculative but founded in practice. For practice should not flow from speculative theory, but theory should flow rather from practice ... When the physician has related the anatomical concordance of the macrocosm and the microcosm, each in their specific place, then it follows that there is a different disease of the leg, another of the flesh, another of the blood, just as there are [certain kinds of] worms in wood, other worms in plants, and still others in leaves. There are as many diseases as there are species.

I. xi. 182-3

7.3

Now alchemy is an art which is necessary and must exist. Because it represents the art of Vulcan, it is important to know what Vulcan can do. Alchemy is an art, Vulcan is its artist ... Now God created all things; He created something out of nothing. That something is a seed, which contains within itself its appointed end, its determination, its office, its task. Just as all things have been created from nothing, there is yet nothing which is completely perfect; that is to say, it has not been finished, but Vulcan must complete it. All things are created as far as we know them, but not as far as they should be. Wood grows, but not into coals or logs; clay grows, but not into earthen pots. Thus it is with all growth, and one should understand the significance of Vulcan. Take an example: God has created iron, but not what can be made from it, namely horseshoes, rods, sickles; He simply gives us iron ore. He then tells the fire and Vulcan what to do: the iron must be separated from the dross and then whatever is to be made should be forged. That is alchemy and the foundryman is called Vulcan; whatever the fire does is alchemy—likewise in the kitchen and in the oven. Thus it is also with medicine: it is created by God but incomplete and buried in the dross . . . The dross must be removed and then the medicine is available. That is alchemy and the office of Vulcan.

I. xi. 186-8

7.4

Take the example of bread. The external art of alchemy in the baker's oven cannot produce ultimate matter, but only intermediate matter. Nature first produces the harvest; then alchemy reaps, mills, and bakes it before it reaches the mouth. At this point prime and intermediate matter have been created; now the alchemy of the microcosm commences. This [alchemy] has prime matter in the mouth: bread. It is chewed and digested, so that it becomes flesh and blood, and thus it is now ultimate matter . . . Thus Nature deals with us as creatures of God . . . Nothing is created as ultimate matter. But all things are created as prime matter and Vulcan converts them through the art of alchemy into ultimate matter. The *Archeus*, the inner Vulcan, follows suit; it knows how to distinguish parts and to circulate and distribute them according to the arts of sublimation, distillation, and reverberation. These arts are also within man just as they are present in external alchemy, which is its model. Thus are Vulcan and the *Archeus* to be distinguished from each other.

I. xi. 188

7.5

God ordained it so. A physician must consider—as God has created nothing in its final form, but simply ordered Vulcan to do his part—how to bring these things to their [appointed] end and not to mix up the dross and the iron. For instance, bread is created and given to us by God, but not as it comes from the baker, but through the three Vulcans, the peasant, the miller, and the baker; they make bread out of it. Thus must medicine operate with the inner Vulcan. Therefore no physician should be ashamed of alchemy. For what I have described can only be achieved by alchemy. Wherever this does not occur, no physician can be present.

I. ix. 189-90

7.6

Now note the difference between *experientia* and *scientia* . . . *Scientia* is inherent in a thing, it is given by God; *experientia* is a knowledge of that in which *scientia* is proven. For instance, the pear tree has *scientia* in itself, and we who see its works have *experientia* of its *scientia* . . . And just as the pear tree retains its own *scientia*, . . . one should understand that God has given each his [particular] *scientia*, whereupon it follows that each should develop his gift and *scientia* to the utmost, alchemically speaking, to the highest degree . . . Each should further his own gift, in order that he reach his end, and not learn his innate *scientia* from other creatures. For this [*scientia*] is given to him alone, not to the others, from whom you think you can learn. Why would the pear tree learn from the sloe tree? Why the fig tree from the thorns? . . . Thus follows the book of *scientia*, that we experience *scientia* . . . It is *scientia* to make a patient healthy. But this *scientia* is the medicine, not the physician . . . These are the books of medicine, in which a physician should establish himself, rather than sitting behind the stove and treating his patients with sophistical logic.

I. xi. 192-5

8

SIEBEN DEFENSIONES (1538)

8.1

A physician must also be a philosopher and see things with the eyes of a philosopher. If he wishes to be such a man, he must stay in those places and regions where his object is. For if one wants to eat a roast, the meat comes from one country, the salt from another, and the meal from yet another. If these things have to travel in order to come to you, so you have to travel until you reach those things which cannot go to you. For the arts have no feet so that the butcher may drive them to you; they cannot be shipped in tubs nor sealed in barrels; and because they have this shortcoming, you must do what they ought to. The English humours are not Hungarian, nor the Neapolitan ones Prussian. Therefore you must go where they are. And the more you seek them there and the more you experience, the greater is your understanding in your own country. The physician must also be an alchemist. If he wishes to be such, he must see the mother [matrix] from which the minerals grow. Now the mountains will not follow him, but he must follow them. Where the minerals are, there also are the artists [experts]; if one wants to seek artists in the separation and preparation of Nature, one must seek them at the place where the minerals are. How can one understand the preparation of Nature if one does not seek it where it is? . . . I need not mention that he who travels here and there, becoming acquainted with many types of people, experiencing many kinds of behaviour and customs, will experience something. A lover will go a long way when he sees a pretty woman, but how much further for a fine piece of knowledge! . . . Those who sit behind the stove eat partridges, and those who follow knowledge eat only milk soup; the merchants wear chains and silk, those who travel can scarcely afford some ticking. Those who sit within the city walls can keep cool and warm as they wish; those in the arts—but for the tree, they would have no shade. Whoever wants to serve his stomach does not follow me; he follows those who go in soft clothes, which would be no use for travelling. For Juvenal has described them—that only he who has nothing wanders merrily. Therefore they also heed the same motto: in order that they will not be murdered, they remain behind the stove and turn pears over. So I think that I have done my travelling properly up until now and consider it an achievement and no disgrace. He who wishes to explore Nature must tread her books with his feet. Writing is learned from letters, but Nature by travelling from country to country. One country, one page. This is the Codex of Nature and thus must its leaves be turned.

I. xi. 144-6

PHILOSOPHY

ASTRONOMIA MAGNA OR THE WHOLE PHILOSOPHIA SAGAX OF THE GREAT AND LITTLE WORLD (1537-8)

9.1

PREFACE

The sagacious philosophy describes the whole religion of all creatures and the classification of their fundamentals and art. If these are to be understood properly, it is necessary to divide them up into their species. Although this classification is neglected by other philosophies, it should not be omitted. Firstly, it is sagacious because God gave unto men all the arts and everything that is natural through the medium of the heavens, because the heavens are the light of Nature. Next, it is useful, for all the necessary arts spring from it. The great art of medicine has its cornerstone in the art of astronomy, as does the disease of man, his health, and his death. Whoever heeds this not is in error. For the physician who does not understand astronomy cannot be called a complete physician, because more than half of all diseases are governed by the heavens. Furthermore this sagacious art is not complete in astronomy but also with respect to the eternal wisdom. Note furthermore that the art of astronomy enables one to understand the innate secrets of the heart and the good and evil in the nature of man. The reason is that man is made out of the Great World and has his nature therein. And because there is one human nature deriving from the earth and another from the heavens, it is necessary to discover what each one says.

I make it abundantly clear that everything in which man is subject to the light of Nature comes from the stars. All natural arts and human wisdom are given by the stars, we are the pupils of the stars, and they our teacher. God has ordered everything in the light of Nature, so that we may learn from it. The false prophets destroy this art, and the false physicians arise from the neglect of this cornerstone. They do not know what the light of Nature teaches, not what God teaches, nor whence come the perishable and the eternal. They do not understand themselves, because supposing and thinking are separated from knowing and ability by art: that is to say, astronomy teaches with great reason how all things come to pass. Whatever is divine is learnt from God; whatever concerns the perishable is learnt from the heavens.

In order that this preface be not unduly long, you should know that many claim to be astronomers. They seek long words but the little pearl of truth is lost. Now I will shortly show you the art of astronomy in nine parts; whoever understands them properly has become an astronomer. As I say to start with, I must show all the species, in order that it is understood that astronomy is the mother of all other arts.

The good physician, the good philosopher, justice, the eternal wisdom, and the light of Nature are grounded in astronomy. Likewise with religion, and no art can be perfected without astronomy. And once we have understood the light of Nature properly, we are more able to understand all things that God works through man . . .

See, friends, how much simple-mindedness and foolishness there is in clever people who have a grasp of something. The astrologer dismisses the magician, the diviner, the reader of signs, the practitioner of uncertain arts; he recognizes only the instrument-maker. But the magician dismisses the astrologer, the instrument-maker, and the reader of signs. But the reader of signs despises all of the other six. The diviner says nothing to the other six. The necromancer does not know the assumptions of the others. The practitioner of uncertain arts considers himself the best. The instrument-maker uses the instruments and gets involved a little everywhere . . . This is why it is necessary to bring them all into a proper order, so that each can be thoroughly understood in its essence . . .

In God there is only one way, one art, one teaching, one manner, one essence . . . but in the light of Nature there are many
ways of working, as craftsman, in the arts, in other faculties,
and in the religions . . . Every art should be complete in itself,
the astrologer should know his art, the magician his, likewise
the diviner, the necromancer, the reader of signs, the practitioner of uncertain arts, the instrument-maker, and the gener-
ators. But noble is he who can grasp as one the whole family
of arts in his brain and bring them all together. He can recognize the miracles of God and read the magnalia [divine works
in Nature] and work with them.

I. xii. 3-7

9.2

There are two kinds of wisdom in this world—one eternal and
one temporal. The eternal wisdom springs directly from the
light of the Holy Ghost, the other wisdom directly from the
light of Nature. The one that comes from the light of the Holy
Ghost is of only one species—it is the just and flawless wisdom. But the one that comes from the light of Nature comprises two species: good and evil. The good wisdom is joined
to the Eternal, the evil to damnation . . . Is it not a great treasure of man to distinguish eternal wisdom from temporal wisdom, because he is the image of God, and to understand that
the mortal is worthless when compared with the eternal? Therefore he should always seek what corresponds to this image, and
know how to distinguish a good and an evil kind of temporal
wisdom. Thus he can accept the evil or the good and yet know
what serves evil and whither the good goes . . . And of this
other wisdom let him retain only the good kind, and reject the
evil kind. For wisdom does not command you, but you alone
command yourself.

I. xii. 8-9

9.3

Why should the Father's light and I be regarded and judged
as heathenish, when I am a Christian and walk in the light of

Christ, both old and new? For if the Father and Son are one, how can I then honour two lights? I would be an idolater. But the number one protects me. And since I love them both, and give to each its light, as God ordained everyone to do, how can I be a heathen? I know well that the light of Nature is not eternal, but that I must become eternal through the eternal light. But might one not combine the mortal light of the soul with the eternal light? The body and the soul are two together. Can one not use the two lights, just as God has given man two essences, the elemental and the eternal, until such time as they are united at the resurrection? Thus the elemental is assigned to the earth, and the eternal to the kingdom of God. I have written as a Christian and am no heathen, I am a German.

I. xii. 10-12

9.4

Man has two bodies: one from the earth, the second from the stars, and thus they are easily distinguishable. The elemental, material body goes to the grave along with its essence; the side-real, subtle body dissolves gradually and goes back to its source, but the spirit of God in us, which is like His image, returns to Him whose image it is. Thus each part dies in that medium from which it has been created, and finds rest accordingly.

I. xii. 18

9.5

Christ and His apostles prophesy the seasons of the nations, but the astronomer prophesies the seasons of Nature. This is a great difference; take good note of it, you naturalists and theologians. For what God prophesies happens and nothing can prevent it. But what the astronomer says, may or may not happen. Thus prophecy springs from one source, astronomy from another. The true knowledge of man's essence can be attained only on the basis of his life; it cannot be understood by any other sign.

I. xii. 119

9.6

The world machine is made of two parts—one tangible and

perceptible, and the other invisible and imperceptible. The tangible part is the body, the invisible is the stars. The tangible part is in turn composed of three parts—Sulphur, Mercury, and Salt; the invisible also consists of three parts—feeling, wisdom, and art. The two parts together constitute life . . . All creatures in the world are made thus; and all creatures are divided into these two parts, the sensible and the insensible. The sensible is twofold, the rational and irrational, but both relate to the animal nature. Men know by reason what they should do and when to do it, they have judgement, whereas the beasts are irrational. All sentient being is governed by the stars, men in a human fashion, the beasts in an animal fashion . . . Human reason in the arts, mood, and wisdom comes to man from the stars; animal nature is simply a matter of eating and drinking. The beasts take their nature from the stars, but man draws his mortal wisdom, reason, and art from the stars—and everything that comes from the light of Nature must be learned from the light of Nature, excepting only the image of God, which is subject to the spirit which the Lord has given to man. The spirit instructs man in supernatural and eternal things, and after the separation of matter from spirit it returns to the Lord. For it is given to man only as a schoolmaster to illuminate him in things eternal.

I. xii. 20-1

9.7

The light of Nature in man comes from the stars, and his flesh and blood come from the material elements. Thus two influences operate in man. The first is the heavenly light in natural wisdom, art, and reason. All these are the children of this father . . . The second influence emanates from matter and includes concupiscence, eating, drinking, and everything that relates to the flesh and blood. Therefore one must not attribute to the stars that which originates in the flesh and blood. For heaven does not make anyone unchaste or greedy . . . From heaven come only wisdom, art, and reason . . . In the stars lie all faculties, all arts, all crafts, all wisdom, all reason, as well as foolishness and whatever pertains to it; for there is nothing in man which does not flow into him from the light of Nature. But what is in the light of Nature is subject to the influence of the stars. The stars are our school in which all these things must be learned.

I. xii. 22-3

9.8

If there had been no Venus, music would never have been invented, and if there had been no Mars, the crafts would never have been invented. Thus the stars teach us all the arts that exist on earth; and if the stars were not active in us, and we had been compelled to do everything by ourselves, no art would ever have come into being ... Just as the constellations of the heavens have been so constantly renewed from the days of Adam down to our own time, so new arts arise from year to year. And not only the arts, but also all wars, all governments, and everything which our brains produce, receive their guidance from the stars now and for ever. And were all musicians and all craftsman to die, this schoolmaster would remain ... and would always instruct new ones.

I. xii. 23

9.9

Not all the stars have yet completed their action and imprinted their influences. Thus, the invention of arts has not yet come to an end. For this reason no one who has discovered something new or who undertakes to explore some unknown field should be held back ... Give heed to those who each day seek something new and also each day find something new, whatever it may be—whether in natural wisdom, arts or custom. For the heavens are responsible for it. Thus new teachings, new arts, new orders, new diseases, new medicine proceed from this, for the heavens are constantly at work. And it remains for man to decide what portion of these things he should take to himself and what he should not.

I. xii. 24-5

9.10

For the ancients had cultivated the spirit of observation (in the light of Nature) and recognized that the heavens were the mother of all human wisdom, whence they derived a great advance in science and the arts. Knowledge and science thus obtained are admittedly limited and transient. Yet it is a divine gift to investigate in the light of Nature. Thus, even before the birth of Christ, the world was endowed with scientific knowledge. But man degenerated, and now he expounds the figments of his own imagination; false wisdom, false arts, and false medicine which have nothing to do with the light of Nature. At the time of Christ this was the intellectual conduct of the Pharisees and scribes, and through their foolishness astronomy was forgotten. Christ taught the eternal wisdom and his miracles overwhelmed the light of Nature; the arts of magic, divination, and other species of astronomy were thus neglected as a lesser light. People thought it was better to follow Christ than to follow Nature, better to be an apostle than a magus, better to be a prophet than an astronomer. Thus Dionysius the Areopagite renounced astronomy at Athens and followed in the steps of St Paul.

I. xii. 26-7

9.11

But logic intervened to extinguish both the light of Nature and the light of wisdom and introduced an alien doctrine which relegated both kinds of wisdom. These people began to extinguish the lights of the eternal and Nature and to darken their truth before the time of Christ. But Christ and His followers took nothing away from the light of Nature, it was the old leaven of the Pharisees who move about in the schools, analyse, and want to break the power of Nature. They follow neither Christ nor the light of Nature. They are the dead who bury the dead; there is no life in their work, because they have no light in which they can learn anything, much as they wish to act as both the natural and eternal lights themselves. Thus has the light of Nature and also that of the Holy Ghost been snuffed out and disregarded.

I. xii. 28

9.12

Natural reason and eternal wisdom belong together. Natural

reason may exist without eternal wisdom, when it follows the heathen way, and is not concerned with the Eternal. But eternal reason cannot exist without natural wisdom, because man must find the eternal in the natural. Therefore a man who dwells in God has both as his guides in all things.

I. xii. 29

9.13

For Holy Scripture represents the beginning of all philosophy and natural science; without this beginning all philosophy would be used and applied in vain. Consequently, if a philosopher is not born out of theology, he has no cornerstone upon which to base his philosophy. For truth springs from theology, and cannot be discovered without its help.

I. xii. 32

9.14

Man was not born out of a nothingness, but was made from a substance . . . The Scriptures prove that God took the *limus terrae* [the primordial stuff of the earth], and formed man out of this mass. Furthermore, they prove that man is ashes and powder, dust and earth; and this proves sufficiently that he is made of the primordial substance . . . This dust is *limus terrae*. But *limus terrae* is also the Great World, and thus man was created from heaven and earth, that is from the upper and lower creations . . . *Limus terrae* is an extract of the firmament and the elements.

I. xii. 33

9.15

After God had created all creatures, elements, and stars in accordance with His will, he finally resolved to make man in the following manner: he took each of the four elements and also extracted the essence of wisdom, art, and reason from the stars. And then he combined both natures, the elemental and the astral, with a *massa* which is known as the *limus terrae* in the Scriptures. Thus two bodies have arisen from this *massa*, the sidereal [astral] and the elemental. And this is called the fifth essence [quintessence] according to the light of Nature; that is to say, the *massa* is extracted and both the firmament and the elements have been combined into one. Thus it follows: what has been extracted from the four [elements] makes the fifth, so that the four are like a mother to the fifth. And moreover, the fifth essence is the whole basis and core of all essences and properties of the whole world; the hand of God held all Nature, virtues, and properties and essences in the upper and lower regions and formed man out of these in His image.

I. xii. 36-7

9.16

The fifth essence is extracted from two bodies and has been combined in one body to form man ... That is to say, man receives heavenly wisdom, reason, and art and such from the stars, and flesh and blood from the elements. Therefore man is the fifth essence, the microcosm and the son of the whole world, because he has been created as an extract of all creation by the hand of God ... Thus man beats like the stars and also like the elements, from which he is made. Just as he has all her properties within himself, so the Great World nourishes and feeds him in wisdom, reason, food, and drink as her own flesh and blood so wonderfully born of her.

I. xii. 39-40

9.17

The wise man is the man who lives by divine wisdom and is an image of Him in whose likeness he was created. The wise man rules over both bodies, the sidereal and the elemental. Man must serve both, he must walk in the ways of each, in order to fulfil the law of the Lord and live in harmony with Nature, and with the will of God and with the divine spirit. He must not prefer the mortal body and its cleverness to the eternal image, nor must he reject this image for the sake of the animal body nor consider the wisdom of the animal body as the eternal holiness ... The wise man lives according to the image of God and not according to the ways of the world. And he who lives according to the image of God will conquer the stars.

I. xii. 41-2

9.18

Just as man originates in the Great World, and is inseparably
bound to it, so has woman been created from man, and cannot separate from him. For if Eve had been formed otherwise
than from the body of man, mutual desire would never have
arisen between them. But because they are of one flesh and
one blood, it follows that they cannot let go of each other.

I. xii. 44

9.19

God willed that the seed of man should not be sown in the
body of the elements, but in woman; that His image should
be conceived in her and born through her and not in the external
creation. And yet woman in her own way is also a field of the
earth and not at all different from it. She replaces it, so to speak,
she is the field, the earth, and the garden in which the child
is sown and planted and then grows up to be a man.

I. xii. 46

9.20

God makes a house; man too can build one. God has hands
and feet in His word, man has them in his limbs. One man
can cure another with medicine, which he must set to work
by means of his body; God does this by one word without
hands and feet. A man walks on his feet, the spirit walks without
feet . . . God wills the earth to grow trees, pears, and other
fruits and creatures of all kinds . . . Similarly He wills that all
the arts—music, the mechanical arts, the faculties, and the doctrines of religion—which He created in the firmament, should
become real . . . And this must be realized through man, just
as the pears are brought to maturity by the tree. For the stars
need an agent through which to work, and this agent is man
and man alone. Man has been so created in such a form that
through him the magnalia of Nature are made visible and given
form.

I. xii. 56-7

9.21

God is moved by such a love to reveal the secrets of the stars, that He created the microcosm, not just to reveal the secrect of the stars through the work of man, but to reveal all natural mysteries of the elements. This could not occur without man. And God wishes that those things which are invisible shall become visible . . . Because God ordained it thus, He does not want man to rest and be indolent, not to stand still . . . but daily to explore the secrets of Nature . . . Thus God created man, in order that His invisible works would be visibly realized, that is through man . . . God does not want His secrets to be [merely] visible; it is His will that they become manifest and knowable through the works of man who has been created in order to make them visible. Thus Christ, whom no one recognized as the second person of the Trinity, was considered by everyone to be a man, because what He actually was remained invisible . . . For man is the revealer of that which is hidden in all things . . . And it is no different with man, for what 'man' is remains hidden and no one sees what is in him, save what his works reveal . . . Therefore man should work continually to discover what God has given him . . . We too should make manifest that which He has put in us, to the end that the unbelievers may see what God can achieve through man.

I. xii. 59–60

9.22

The difference in form and shape between the two bodies, the visible and the invisible, the material and the eternal, is as great as the difference between their natures . . . They are like a married couple, one in the flesh, but twofold in their nature . . . And because this is so, a contradiction dwells in man . . . Namely, the stars have a different mind, a different mood, a different intention than the lower elements; and on the other hand, these elements have a different mind and mood than the stars. For instance: the elemental, material man wants to live in luxury and lewdness; the astral, ethereal body, the inner counterpart of the upper sphere, wants to study, learn, pursue arts, and so on. As a result there arises an antagonism in man himself. The visible, material body wants one thing, and the invisible, ethereal body wants another thing, neither is like the other . . . Therefore there dwells in each of these bodies an urge to exceed what is given to it, and neither wants to follow a middle course and act with measure . . . thus enmity arises between them. For everything that exceeds its measure brings destruction.

I. xii. 62-3

9.23

THE FOURTH CHAPTER

HOW MANY KINDS OF ASTRONOMY THERE ARE, THEIR ORDER AND PROCESS, AND HOW THESE TOGETHER WITH THEIR MEMBERS MAY BE RECOGNIZED, AND HOW THESE MEMBERS ARE DIVIDED UP INTO THEIR SPECIES

Because I am attempting to outline the influence, concordance, and convenience of outer things on man, it will be helpful to divide them into figures. It is very important to understand the differences between the four figures, and how each one proceeds from the other—this will give you the simplest and clearest explanation of all the following effects. The [second] figure shows how each astronomy consists of members. The [third] figure describes the species of each member, giving a particular explanation of the influences, members, and species, in order that the philosophy can be understood and learned in the most thorough fashion.

The first figure. There are four categories of astronomy and no one resembles another. But because their operation is similar, they are justly all called influences. You can see from the figure how these four influences unite, concord, impress, and operate with respect to man, each according to its nature and property:

The first figure

There are four categories of astronomy

- Natural
- Supera
- Olympi Novi
- Inferorum

Natural Astronomy

This astronomy comes from heaven and was created by God the Father, and it is a science which was assigned and transferred to the microcosm, which is made from the *limus terrae*.

Supera

This astronomy has its seat in heaven and is given to all those who shall rise again from the dead. It has its origin in Christ and it is practised, used, and administered by Him.

Olympi Novi

This astronomy derives from faith: whatever the natural heavens can do, this astronomy can achieve by faith, and it is used by and given to the faithful; it is practised and made manifest by them.

Inferorum

This astronomy has its origin in the natural heavens but it is used only by the demonic spirits, because they are natural astronomers, who can make its species manifest through themselves and through men in the most able fashion.

The second figure shows that there are four kinds of astronomy, each with its special order, and none like another, but ultimately they all come into one way. Now there are nine members in all astronomy, which can be used as sciences by man or other agents. Thus all astronomy has four sciences, and in each of these sciences there are nine members; although the members resemble each other in the various sciences, they are used differently in each case.

The second figure

These are the four kinds of astronomy, which each have nine members, and each kind of astronomy is used accordingly.

Naturalis
Supera
Olympi Novi
Satanistae

Magia
Nigromantia
Nectromantia
Astrologia
Signatum
Artes incertae
Medicina
Adepta
Philosophia
Adepta
Mathematica
Adepta

This is the number of members in the four kinds of astronomy, neither less nor more, through which all forms of astronomy must be practised.

The third figure. Furthermore these are the species of the members, and each member is divided up into a number of species:

The third figure

Magia
1. Description of the supernatural stars
2. Transcription of one living body into another
3. Preparation of the characters and similar benedictions
4. Preparation of the Gamaheu to give them their powers
5. Preparation of the pictures, how they are to be made
6. Cabalistica together with the Cabalia and its powers

Nigromantia
1. The sidereal and elemental spirit, how to recognize them after death
2. How to command both these spirits
3. How to direct the natural Operations Meteorice
4. How a man may be injured without a lesion of the body
5. How a thing becomes invisible and its uses

Nectromantia
1. Visiones Speculares
2. The art Berillistica
3. Thesaurinella
4. Abstracta retraherè
5. Abscondita invenire
6. Adech Plumbeus
7. Virgulta directa
8. Adech Somnialis

Nectromantia
- 9. Ars Lucis
- 10. Superstitio indirecta
- 11. Artes transversae
- 12. Carbonis Speculum
- 13. Scientiae perversae
- 14. Ars literata

Astrologia
- 1. Summus Motor
- 2. Stellarum Cursus
- 3. Firmamenti Natura
- 4. Astorum Operatio
- 5. Conceptionem declarare
- 6. Concordantia cum Elementi
- 7. Coelorum Proprietates
- 8. Prognosticationes Tempestatum
- 9. Prognosticationes Temporales
- 10. Prognosticationes Indiciales
- 11. Prognosticationes Accidentales
- 12. Prognosticationes Medicae
- 13. Novae generationis ventura

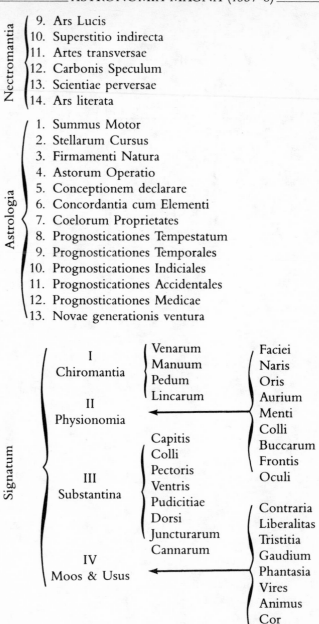

Signatum

I Chiromantia
- Venarum
- Manuum
- Pedum
- Lincarum

II Physionomia
- Faciei
- Naris
- Oris
- Aurium
- Menti
- Colli
- Buccarum
- Frontis
- Oculi

III Substantina
- Capitis
- Colli
- Pectoris
- Ventris
- Pudicitiae
- Dorsi
- Juncturarum
- Cannarum

IV Moos & Usus
- Contraria
- Liberalitas
- Tristitia
- Gaudium
- Phantasia
- Vires
- Animus
- Cor
- Jngenium

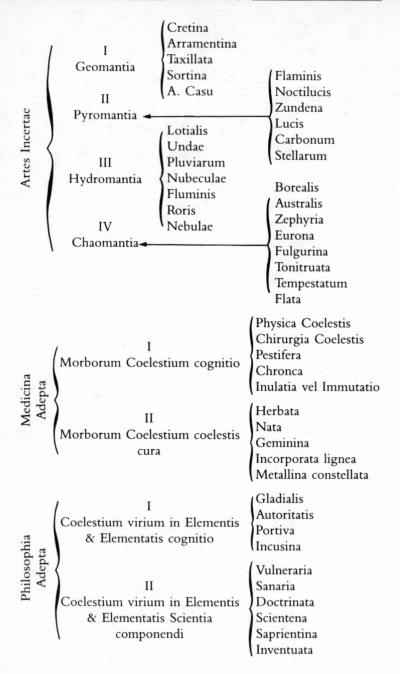

Artes Incertae

I Geomantia
- Cretina
- Arramentina
- Taxillata
- Sortina
- A. Casu

II Pyromantia
- Flaminis
- Noctilucis
- Zundena
- Lucis
- Carbonum
- Stellarum

III Hydromantia
- Lotialis
- Undae
- Pluviarum
- Nubeculae
- Fluminis
- Roris
- Nebulae

IV Chaomantia
- Borealis
- Australis
- Zephyria
- Eurona
- Fulgurina
- Tonitruata
- Tempestatum
- Flata

Medicina Adepta

I Morborum Coelestium cognitio
- Physica Coelestis
- Chirurgia Coelestis
- Pestifera
- Chronca
- Inulatia vel Immutatio

II Morborum Coelestium coelestis cura
- Herbata
- Nata
- Geminina
- Incorporata lignea
- Metallina constellata

Philosophia Adepta

I Coelestium virium in Elementis & Elementatis cognitio
- Gladialis
- Autoritatis
- Portiva
- Incusina

II Coelestium virium in Elementis & Elementatis Scientia componendi
- Vulneraria
- Sanaria
- Doctrinata
- Scientena
- Saprientina
- Inventuata

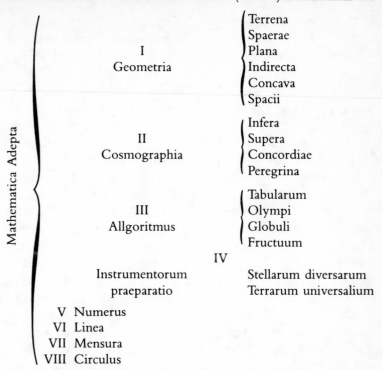

If one wishes to be a perfect astronomer, one must understand and recognize these species. Here follows an explanation of what the members and their constituent species can do.

Explanation of *magica* and its species: *magica* is divided into six species. The beginning of magic is an explanation of the unnatural signs and how one may recognize them both supernaturally in heaven and also naturally, as in the case of the star over Bethlehem. This star stood among the other stars as Christ wandered on earth as a man among other men. The stars will be recognized only by the magi, just as Christ was recognized only by his own kind. Thus the magi are interpreters of the supernatural signs in heaven, just as the Apostles were exponents of Christ. Thus the magi are also interpreters of all prophecies and the apocalyptic revelation. This is the species of magical art and is called the *insignis magica*. There is a further species of magic which occurred at the time of Moses and concerns the transformation of one body into another. It is simi-

lar to the process by which Christ was transfigured and illuminated like the sun. So should this magic be understood and
this species is called *magica transfigurativa*. The third species
teaches how to make words which can summon the powers
of heaven. For example: this species can achieve by words everything that the physician is able to achieve through medicine.
This species is called *characteralis*. The fourth species teaches how
to make cameos and gems which can achieve all that is possible by natural means. For example, a key opens a lock, a sword
cuts wounds, a suit of armour protects from stabbing and shoot-
ing; thus the fourth species of magic can do invisibly by art
what Nature can do visibly. This species is called *gamaheos*. The
fifth species teaches how to make pictures which will bring
about what they portray. Whatever can be done naturally can
be done with this magic: just as Nature can bring great pain,
paralyse, blind, or render a man impotent, and also make certain men healthy again, so too can this magic do, and it is called
altera in alteram. Magic can also make it possible for one to hear
another's voice from the other side of the ocean, and also for
one in the West to talk with another in the East. If Nature enables one to hear a voice a hundred paces away, this species enables one to hear it a hundred German miles off. And just as
Nature makes it possible for a messenger or a steed to travel
a certain distance in a month, this species can make it possible
within a day. Whatever Nature requires a year for, this magic
can achieve it in a month. This species is called *ars cabalistica*.
These six species constitute the magical art . . .

Explanation of *nigromantia* and its species: *nigromantia* is divided
into five species. Firstly, following the death of a man, there
remain two mortal spirits on earth, the elemental and the sidereal. Whoever understands these two spirits, their properties,
nature, and behaviour, is proficient in the first species of nigromancy, which is called *cognito mortalem*. Whoever can deal with
these mortal spirits and command them to do his business is
proficient in the second species of nigromancy. It is possible
to treat the abandoned spirit as a servant, and this species is
called *tortura noctis*. The third species concerns the spirits which
are born in the heavens and hover in chaos before dying and

being born again. Now whoever can exploit these spirits as
a physician can exploit herbs is proficient in the third species
of nigromancy, which is called *meteorica vivens*. Whoever can
injure a man without making an opening in his body, just as
one can seize a fish out of water without making a hole or put
something into water without making a hole, is proficient in
the fourth species of nigromancy: that is, he can withdraw
something from and insert something in the body. This species is called *clausura nigromantica*. Whoever knows how to make
a visible body invisible and conceal it as the night can make
a man invisible is proficient in the fifth species of nigromancy,
and this is called *obcaecatio nigromantica*.

Explanation of *nectromantia* [*sic*] and its species: *nectromantia* is
divided into fourteen species. The first of these several kinds
is knows as *visiones* and may be understood by an example: a
master has a servant, to whom he entrusts all his secrets. Now
if one wishes to know these secrets and the master will not
reveal them, one must learn them from the servant. One may
similarly understand nectromancy [*sic*] as a means of knowing
the hidden secrets of men. A man may think that he is quite
alone, but there is something present, which we cannot see,
in all our words and works. This thing is privy to the secrets
of man and is called *flaga* [familiar spirit]. Whoever is able to
subdue them and make them obedient to his will, as one might
the servant of a master, is proficient in nectromancy. Now
although there are many kinds of species in this member, these
are just two types. The first consists in the *flagae* becoming visible, the second in their effecting the nectromantic will unseen.
It is the art of knowing the secrets of men, as far as it is possible to do outside their hearts. An example: whatever a man does
not keep within himself but tells to another is unconcealed from
this art—and whatever he physically does is not secret. For it
follows that whatever is spoken or done is evident to the *flagae*, and the nectromancer is able to understand them. Now
here is an explanation of how they are to be understood. One
must encourage them or force them to reveal such secrets, as
one would with a secretary. One can make the *flagae* obedient
and also visible by means of a mirror, glass, and coals. And

it can be done invisibly by pointing and signing with the finger. Thus one can find hidden treasures; thus one can read sealed letters; thus can things hidden be laid bare; thus one can find the place where something lies hidden; and thus can things be summoned which were lost. Whoever can subject the *flagae* to his will to reveal the secrets of man and whatever he has hidden can practise nectromancy and is a perfect nectromancer. And whatever cannot be done pleasantly can be done with violence. Thus nectromancy is an art of acting pleasantly or violently. For just as a man must be subject to the Emperor and ruled by the sword, so it is possible to compel the *flagae* to manifest in mirrors, glasses, coals, and nails, and also to give indications by means of divining-rods, lead, and stone, etc. Also by making candles go out, so that secrets are revealed.

Explanation of *astrologia* and its species: (*astrologia* is divided into thirteen species). In order to understand what astrology and an astrologer are, note this example. Just as one can recognize how men run about on earth, to and fro, one upright, another hobbling, so one may understand the motions of the stars, and such a person is proficient in astrology. But there is more to it than that: one should know what the goal of this motion is just as one might send a messenger with a specific errand and know what he is about. Or just as one may know what a craftsman will achieve in any given day, so should the astrologer know what each star intends to do as its work. Whoever knows that is a better astrologer than one who just knows how they move amongst themselves. It is also good to know what they can achieve and what they cannot. For man begins much that he cannot complete. You should understand that in the heavens the stars begin much which cannot be completed, just as men do. For the stars and men have similar capacities. Whoever knows men's movements knows their intentions, knows what can be finished and what cannot. Astrology can pride itself on the same understanding, for it follows that the astrologer recognizes the *summum motorem* [supreme mover] and knows that nature is in its hands. He also knows that he cannot change the heavens as can the supreme mover. The astrologer should know the innate nature of the stars, their

nature, complexion, and property, as well as a physician understands the nature of a patient, and also the concordance of the
stars, how they stand in relation to men, animals, the four elements, and all things that grow and spring from the matrices
of the elements. Whoever knows this, has authority to talk about
astrology. Know furthermore that the astrologer should be able
to find his bearings in the heavens with the aid of his natural
reason, in a natural way, as a philosopher or a physician finds
his way among the things of Nature, which derive from the
elements. But he should not have a higher opinion of this art
nor place more reliance on it than behoves a prisoner. The
prisoner, too, has all the qualities that belong to a man, but
he is prevented from unfolding them; he cannot do what he
wants. The same is true of the heavens: they lie imprisoned
in the hand of the supreme mover, and what this hand intends
is hidden from the astrologer. Although astrology is a member of astronomy, the art can be impeded, furthered, or changed
by the hand of the supreme mover. But whoever knows and
understands the natural properties of the stars outside the hand
of the supreme mover is an astrologer and can practise astrology.

Explanation of *signatum* and its species: (*signatum* is divided into
four species). There is nothing that Nature has not signed in
such a way that man may discover its essence. . . the stars have
their motions by which they are known. The same is true of
man, save that they give him fixed lines by which one can establish the motion. And just as the motion of the stars has a complexion, so does the line of man. As you can see, each herb
is given the form that befits its nature; similarly man is endowed
with a form corresponding to his inner nature. And just as the
form shows what a given herb is, so the human sign indicates
what a given man is. This does not refer to the name, sex, or
similar characteristics, but to the properties inherent in the man.
The art of signatures teaches us to give each being its true name
in accordance with its innate nature. A wolf must not be called
a sheep, a dove must not be called a fox; each being should
receive a name that accords with its nature. Through these four
species Nature makes apparent all the natural secrets which lie
in man. Since nothing is so secret or hidden that it cannot be

revealed, everything depends on the discovery of those things which manifest the hidden. It follows that chiromancy understands the signatures of such secrets, and the nature of each man's soul accords with these lines and veins. The same is true of the face, which is shaped and formed according to the content of the mind and soul, and the same is again true of the proportions of the human body. Thus can this member of astronomy describe each kind of soul. For the sculptor of Nature is so artful that he does not fashion the soul to fit the form, but the form to fit the soul; that is to say, the shape of a man is formed in accordance with the manner of his heart. Nature does not work like a painter who finishes a picture and gives it no signature, because the picture has none within it; it is like a shadow with no power. And yet, lacking power, the art proceeds from the Maker of living beings. And the more accomplished an artist would be, the more necessary it is that he master the art of signatures. The basis of these arts lies in these three species. The fourth species concerns the habits and behaviour of man, and whoever has knowledge of this is a consummate artist in signatures.

Explanation of *artes incertae*: (these comprise four species). These are several long-practised arts which have come down to us from the ancients; these arts are closely akin to magic and are held in great respect; the older they are, the more respected. Although the arts have not become more wicked, man and his soul have, and much depends on man. I call them uncertain arts, though they would have been certain arts at the time of the ancients. These arts are the sixth member of astronomy and treat of great wonderful secrets, which can be understood more quickly than the other members. The basis of their art is mixed as a hand casts lots. Just as the stars and the elements can work through the medium of men's hands and limbs, so each man is a prophet of the natural light. Some prophecies are spoken orally, others made by gestures, other by signs, others by pictures and figures and in many other ways. Because man has these powers of divination, he is able to employ these uncertain arts. And although geomancy takes its name from the earth, pyromancy from fire, hydromancy from water, and chaomancy from the air, their basis lies not in the particular element but in the innate divinatory capacity of man. And just as God has worked through many kinds of people, both humble and important, letting His son wander the earth as a humble man, who chose humble people as His apostles, and humble people have been prophets, so great miracles can happen through such humbleness and so can such people be prophets in geomancy, pyromancy, hydromancy, and chaomancy. It depends on whether the man has this divinatory nature. A practitioner of the uncertain arts must choose the right moment. Know the varieties of the uncertain arts: a geomancer works with chalk, dice, wishes, and questions; pyromancy is practised by speculations in the fire; the portents of water consist in waves, foam, and bubbles; the verdict of air in the direction of the wind, whether it be straight or turbulent.

Explanation of *Medicina Adepta*: (this comprises two species). Adept medicine is that medicine which derives from the heavens. There are two kinds of medicine and two kinds of disease: one heavenly and the other elemental. Whoever understands heavenly disease and its medicine can practise adept medicine. Two species can be distinguished in this member: stellar physics and stellar surgery. Physics assumes that nothing is without disease and the stars themselves are not healthy. And because these things are our nourishment, we become like them. One should understand stellar surgery in a similar way. A star can wound, just as swords do, not in the form of cuts but in openings on the body in accordance with the heavenly sword. The appropriate medicine must be applied to these diseases, for in these cases elemental medicine will be of no avail. Remedies originate and grow in the stars just as they do in the earth, but there is a difference. The medicine of the elements has a tangible body in which its virtue lies; the medicine of heaven has no body, but is alone, independent, separate, and purified, its needs no alchemist to separate the pure from the impure, or to extract the quintessence from the four elements. It is a medicine which requires no additives or cooking but can be directly administered to the patient. Whoever understands the diseases which come from heaven and knows how to cure them with heavenly medicine is called *medicus adeptus*. That is intelligent medicine and the basis of half its province. For the heavens are connected with the body in such a way that infection can travel from the invisible realm to the visible, but the visible has no effect on the invisible.

Explanation of *Philosophia Adepta*: (this comprises two species). All earthly bodies carry a heavenly virtue in addition to that which they have from the elements. The adept philosopher can discern the heavenly virtue in an earthly body. Just as a common philosopher can describe the natural virtues of the herbs, so can an adept philosopher describe their heavenly virtues. This cannot be determined by means of alchemy, which is effective in the elemental case. For whatever the alchemist breaks down loses its heavenly virtue. If the heavenly virtue is to be effective, no decomposition must occur. Know furthermore that adept philosophy is cognizant of a special art of composition. Just as one can mix many kinds of bodies, so can the sidereal arcana be combined. This is how the names *tyriaca coelestis, methridatum Olympi* and *suffuff aethereum* are derived. Just as they are physically made, so they can be combined in a heavenly fashion. Note that such heavenly virtues produce knives and swords which can hew an anvil in two and cut through any metal as if it were wax; this art is called *gladialis* or *incusiva*. Just as the elemental art makes knives to cut wood, so the astral art makes knives to cut metal. Know also that just as Nature makes natural keys to open locks, adept philosophy makes invisible keys. For whatever the elements can achieve in their realm through bodies, the star can do in its own essence. That is *philosophia autoritatis* and also *portiva*, because it is conveyed in an elemental body. As you can see, wounds can be healed naturally by elemental medicine, so you should know that healing can occur astrally, and every disease can be healed thus as through elemental virtues. This is how one should understand the sciences of *vulnerari* and *sanaria* in the heavens. Note also that *philosophia adepta* is more than doctrine and science. You can understand this so: just as a pupil learns from his schoolmaster, so man must learn adept philosophy from the heavenly preceptors. Scholarship is the species *doctrinata*, art is the species *scientena*. Whatever one man can learn from another, he can learn more thoroughly and with more understanding from the stars. Thus is the species of *sapientena* to be understood. It is also possible to discover new arts through adept philosophy and this is the species *inventuata*, also in the stars. One must take them wherever they are. Thus inventions come forth, and this is the right way to make man perfect in the light of Nature.

Explanation of *Mathematica Adepta*: (this comprises eight species). The eight members described so far cannot be effected without instruments; mathematics is the art which teaches how to make such instruments. Thus there are mathematics corresponding to magic, nigromancy, nectromancy, astrology, signatures, uncertain arts, adept medicine, and adept philosophy. Firstly, there are three species by means of which the instruments are prepared. One is geometry and that has six parts: a geometry for measuring the earth and making an instrument out of it; a geometry of the heavens for counterfeiting the heavens onto another body, just as an artist counterfeits a thing with colours. Geometry teaches everything about what is flat, smooth, hollow, near, or distant. Likewise with cosmography, which has two particular species, one heavenly and the other elemental, by means of which one can establish how and what anything is. So that if a herb or a bird is seen, one knows how and what it is. One must also know the cosmography of the elements and the stars. . . There is also a cosmography *concordiae*, which teaches how to harmonize both kinds of cosmography, each herb in its star, each star in its herb. And then there is a cosmography *peregrina*, which teaches how to recognize *mobilia*. This is how the mathematics of cosmography should be understood. There is also a mathematics of algorithms, which does not only teach how to compute the forms and bodies and figures, but that the art of arithmetic in all its virtues, number, line, and measure can be used in both cosmographies and geometries. Also that the mathematics *circuli* with all its species derive from the circle. Know accordingly that universal mathematics is the first beginning of the other eight members, and the more thoroughly it is understood, the more effective are the other eight members.

Know now that the nine members and their species have been sufficiently explained, and that these nine members, nine arts, nine sciences can be practised outside the elemental realm and just as naturally as the elemental art. Just as a craftsman completes his task in a physical fasion, so can things occur in a spiritual fashion. Just as one can say that smithery and other crafts are natural arts and are performed and understood naturally, so the members of astronomy are practised naturally. Just as one can say that man is a natural body, so there are natural spirits. Whatever is done by flesh and blood, is done naturally; and likewise, whatever the spirit does, it does naturally. Every body completes the task for which it was created. There is one operation in flesh and blood, another in the spirit. What flesh and blood do is natural; what the spirit does is also natural, what the elements do is natural, what the star does is natural. Elements behave as elements, the heavens as heavens. Whoever is experienced and learned in the elements can philosophize elementally. Whoever is learned in the heavens can philosophize in a heavenly fashion.

I. xii. 75-101

9.24

These nine members of astronomy are all arts, which is to say that they can only be practised by men. Thus there is a human science of magic, one of nigromancy, and one for all the others. Now take note that there are ten more members of astronomy which are not human arts but ethereal arts. That is, the heavens themselves are an astronomer and can practise without the aid of man. Man can see what the heavens have achieved on their own. It is easy to understand these ten members and their species in the special figure shown here. Thus one can understand the capacities of man in the three foregoing figures and the capacities of the heavens in the following figure:

The fourth figure

Figura Scientiarum Astronomiae

1. Divinatio:
   - Somnus
   - Phantasia
   - Speculatio
   - Animus
   - Sensus
   - Vox

2. Augurium:
   - Volatilium
   - Quadrupedum
   - Aquaticorum
   - Vermium
   - Figurarum
   - Monstrorum

3. Ebriecatum:
   - Mania
   - Phrenesis
   - Phantasmata
   - Imaginatio
   - Immutatio

4. Inclinatio:
   - In Carnem
   - in Animum
   - in Spiritum
   - in Doctrinam
   - in Mechanicam
   - in Habilitatem

5. Impressio:
   - Conceptio
   - Partus
   - Sanitas
   - Aegritudo
   - Mores
   - Actus
   - Sapientia
   - Prudentia

6. Generatio:
   - Aquarum Crescentia
   - Terrarum Crescentia
   - Ignis Crescentia
   - Aeris Tereniabin

7. Inanimatum:
   - Nympharum
   - Gigantum
   - Lemurum
   - Gnomorum
   - Sylvestrium
   - Vulcani
   - Umbraginum

8. Meteorica:
   - Pluviarum
   - Roris
   - Pruinae
   - Fulgures
   - Tonitrui
   - Nivis
   - Grandinis
   - Glaciei

9. Aegrorum:
   - Tempestatum
   - Ventorum
   - Alterationum

10. Novalia:
   - In Pennatis
   - in Brutis
   - in Piscibus
   - in Monstris
   - in Transversis
   - in Contrariis

Innatae Prophetiae

Divinatio and its species: to know the future is the greatest secret of all. There are two ways in which one can know the future: firstly by natural means, through prognostications and the verdicts of astronomy; secondly by supernatural means as in prophecies and vaticinations. Divination is the member which describes the supernatural means of foretelling the future and as such occurs through six processes: dreams, fantasies, speculations, the mood, reflection, and the voice. In order that you may understand divination more easily, I shall give several examples. For the most part divinations appear to man in such an unimpressive form that they are ignored. And yet Joseph discovered in his sleep who Mary was and by whom she was with child. And because dreams are not sufficiently heeded, no faith is put in their revelations, although they are in fact divinations. Future events can also be revealed by fantasies in the form of pictures or images. One may encounter strange figures in heaven or spirits. These are all species of divination, but because no one knows whence they come they are mocked. In the case of speculation one thinks how matters may turn out, and if it does so happen, but there is no other reason to account for it, this too will not be believed. Something may be evident in one's mood and in the end it happens. One may frequently think and reflect on something and then it finally happens. Also one may speak of a thing and it happens. But because there are no reasons for the occurrence, the prophecies of divination are scorned—and they also frequently happen through simple and modest people and they too are scorned. So divination is a work that comes from heaven above in the six species indicated, and one should take note of it and not scorn. For a wise man does not scorn them but considers them with wisdom.

Augurium and its species: this also has a supernatural origin and is but the presage of future things. There are six species of auguries, and although they appear ridiculous, the wise man must not scorn them, but recall that Christ appeared in a humble form and was ridiculed. If he understands that inconspicuous things must not be ridiculed but judged with wisdom, he will also be given the understanding to know Christ. The scorners have no understanding, but the wise possess the understanding that God has conferred upon them. The supreme mover gives auguries through particular indications, like the birds, for example, and the wise man can discern that these indications concern men. Thus are plague, war, and murder often presaged. The animals can also feel something unusual which is a presage for man. One can see auguries in the movements of fish in the water, also in worms, wooden figures, and stones. Monsters are frequently born of birds, beasts, fish, worms, and even men, and these are a presage of a future calamity that will come upon man.

Ebriecatum and its species: this member refers to when a man loses his normal reason and acquires an alien reason. For there are two kinds of reason: human reason and alien reason. God gives man human reason, in order that he can conduct his life properly, recognize, measure, and understand things. But with alien reason a man cannot understand things properly, but flies to and fro like a reed in the water. This alien reason is a spirit of giddiness which makes everything mad and confusing. Consider this example of the differences between the two types of reason. A man might live blamelessly according to human reason. But if he was full of wine and drunk, so the human reason would decrease and the alien reason increase. A drunken man does not act out of human reason but is mad, incomprehensible, coarse, and capricious. Now within this member there are five species, by means of which a man may enter a state of alien reason as if he were drunk. For there are such wines in the heavens, and whoever drinks of them falls into the alien, mad, and incomprehensible reason. One species is called *ebriecata mania* or *inebriata mania*, and in this state men read out words and interpret them irrationally. There is *inebriata phrenesis*, and in this state men want to fight out everything with swords. There is *inebriata phantasmata*, an alien reason which has its own strange customs and gestures. There is also a species called *imaginatio inebriata*, in which one thinks that the walls are talking, that one's bed is going round in circles, and one does not know oneself. The fifth species is *immutatio*, when ideas and thoughts are all reversed, friend and foe confused. There might be a hundred such persons gathered together, and they would all think differently and have their own ideas.

Inclinatio and its species: this fourth member concerns the stars' government and influence over man. A star undertakes a thing and wants a man to manifest it. But because no man stands in a conjunction with the star, the star must choose a man like an adoptive son. This inclination occurs in six different ways. It can happen through the body, making a particularly pleasant person, who is also commendable or malignant to other men; Solomon was such an adoptive son with respect to the person. It can happen through the mood, so that a man can surpass all others in mood; Julius Caesar was such an adoptive son with respect to the mood. There are inclinations which can extol the spirit, which then surpasses other spirits in good fortune, and Emperor Barbarossa was such an adoptive son. The stars can also manifest a doctrine through men, and Albertus Magnus, Lactantius, and Wycliffe were such adoptive sons. The stars can prepare a particular art or business ability, and such adoptive sons were Albertus Dürer of Nuremberg and Fugger of Augsburg. In the sixth species the stars confer a dexterity in which persons surpass all others, and the adoptive sons in this case are those who can walk the tightrope. Thus the fourth member and its species relate to the heavenly motions' effects on their adoptive sons. That is inclination.

Impressio and its species: impression is a virtue which comes from the stars and only serves in the elemental body, having nothing in common with the astral body. Just as colours and a body belong together, so the impression and the elemental body cannot be separated. Impression begins with conception, is embodied and grows up with the body. Just as the body has colours, which change over time, as black, red, or blond hair becomes grey or white, so the impression is received by man in the elemental body, ages, and is transformed. Now the impression of the elemental body is the *spiraculum vitae* [breath of life], without which there is no life in the body. The breath of life has two inspirations: God who gives man life, and the innate essence of life. But there is a further inspirator which works together with these. . . Impression is nothing but the permanent inspiration, received at conception and birth, and from this impression follow health or disease, delightful manners, gestures, works, wisdom, and consideration.

Generatio and its species: this member has four species corresponding to each of the four elements. Generation is nothing but the communication which the stars impart to man. The Sun gives warmth to the elements, without it they would all be dead. The Sun is the breath of life to the elements. Now the elements are matrices, the heavens parents; the two give birth to all fruits which grow from the elements, and the Sun is their breath of life. Generation means that the elements can do nothing without the stars, for the elements are matrices, Vulcan is the Sun, Nature is the fabricator. The seeds lie in the matrix and not in the creator, just as the egg is in the hen and not the cock. But if a chick is to be hatched, that must happen through the cock. Thus the matrices have the seed, but the effective power comes from the stars. Concerning generation you should know that all minerals, salts, metals, gems, stones, and rocks grow from the element Water; Water is their mother and the Sun hatches them in the water. The Sun cooks and incubates the fruits of the element Fire, which are all the meteoric impressions: rain, snow, wind, thunder, and hail. All the fruits of the element Earth—wood, herbs, grass, sponges, flowers, and other things—are incubated by the Sun and receive their appropriate nourishment from the stars and the earth. The same is also true of the fruits of the air like tereniabin and manna.

Inanimatum and its species: this member is harder to understand than the others. *Inanimatum* is a man who has no soul, and there are six varieties: nymphs (water creatures), giants, lemurs (mountain creatures), gnomes (air creatures), vulcans (fire creatures), and pygmies or scrats. For just as we men are born on earth with souls, there are those without a soul in each of the four elements and two more besides, the giants and the pygmies. For just as we walk upon the earth but not in it, pass over the water but not in it, across fire and not in it, across the air and not in it, there are men counterfeited in the elements which dwell in them rather than over or upon them, like the phoenix in the fire, the talpa in the earth... These beings are born of heavenly and elemental seeds and not made from the *limus terrae*. These are not creatures but [beings spontaneously generated] like the horse-flies from horse-dung.

Meteorica and their species: this member has many kinds of species and is really the *sagax meteorica*, not the *meteorica minor*. So that you may understand the differences between these two kinds of *meteorica*, you should know that the *meteorica minor* relates to the member of generation, while the manifestations of *meteorica sagax* are born in the sublime Olympus-like rain in the form of a mist, which is spiritual rather than physical. They also cause thunder and lightning, which does not strike the earth but causes globules and stones to fall. The *sagax meteorica* also gives birth to blood, metals, dragons, haloes, apparitions, mirages, figures, and such like.

Aegrorum and its species: the heavens work in many ways. If a tree is cut down at an unpropitious time, the heavens have a power over this tree, and all the aspects and conjunctions of the heavens can be discerned in its wood like the parts of a clock. Similarly, a piece of clay dug up under a particular constellation produces crickets which relate to that constellation, for they change with the Moon... If a man falls sick under such a heavenly power, the astrologer can predict its coming. He can tell more than the crickets in the clay, maggots in the cheese, worms in the wood, and these men are born prophets through their diseases. The species of foretelling concern the weather, whether it is colder or warmer, light or heavy, long or short, when the Moon is new or old, and so on. Nature gives us to understand things through the elemental bodies in the heavens. Thus you can also know the future of the winds, the improvement of the climate. This is the ninth member of the astral sciences.

Novalia and their species: God has ordered how everything should give birth to another, and it pleased God that all things were good. However, it can happen that this order is broken and that deformities appear, but these are only errors of Nature. But it is recognized that the astral nature can cause such things.

For example, a hundred men may be given a task, that each should make an image. No single one is like another, but only the one who can do it well produces a good picture; the other ninety-nine produce nothing good. Likewise Nature practises her art in making man and other living beings, but because there are so many things which make up a man, it is possible that one comes along with its pattern and spoils the work. It is like a council chamber full of folk and each wants his counsel to be followed; the final decision is foolish and cretinous. Understand thus the nature and property of the stars, that they do not act in unison and can produce a mixed result in mind and body, not just in mankind but among the birds, the beasts, the fish, the plants, and the trees contrary to their nature. The naturalist should beware of these monstrous forms because they have a monstrous sense as in madmen, mistletoe, and mould. And where there are such monstrous bodies in Nature, one should seek the monstrous remedies. But these should not be used in the normal body, for imperfect bodies give imperfect medicaments. This is the tenth member of astral science and simply comprises the heavenly influence which transfigures elemental bodies into a perverse and contrary form.

I. xii. 101-17

[The remainder of the *Philosophia Sagax*, a substantial work consisting of four books, extends the discussion of astronomy according to the framework of nine human members and ten heavenly (ethereal) members in all its ramifications. The remaining chapters 6-11 of the first book deal with probations (experiments) in the nine members of magic, nigromancy, nectromancy, astrology, signatures, uncertain arts, adept medicine, adept philosophy, and adept mathematics, and with the ten divine gifts of divination, auguries, *ebriecatum*, inclination, impression, generation, *inanimatum, meteorica, aegrorum*, and *novalia*. However, this first book covers only the first of the four categories of astronomy: natural astronomy. The second book is devoted to the second category, heavenly astronomy, and discusses such matters as the origins of the soul, the mortal and eternal bodies of man, and the relationship of God with man, together with an analogous exposition of the nine members of astronomy and their species, the ten heavenly members, the experiments in the nine members, and the corresponding experiments in the divine gifts, all in the context of heavenly astronomy. This second book comprises nine chapters, the last of which is lost. The third book was devoted to the third category of astronomy, the *Olympi Novi*, but no part of it has survived. The fourth book is devoted to the fourth category of astronomy, infernal astronomy, and comprises thirteen chapters. These deal with the nature of hell; the infernal spirits; the alliance of evil spirits with God, the angels, the Saints, and men; the alliance of the dead with demons, and lastly, an outline of infernal astronomy in the nine members. The complete work thus presents a comprehensive account of what Paracelsus called astronomy, effectively a pansophy of heaven and earth, in a formal structure of categories and encyclopaedic detail.]

9.25

Human nature is different from all other animal nature. It is endowed with divine wisdom, endowed with divine arts. Therefore we are justly called gods and the sons of the All Highest. For the light of Nature is in us and this light is God. Our mortal bodies are vehicles of the divine wisdom. We also have in our power arts that we owe to no one but God, and they are given to us in the hour of our conception... For this reason there are no grounds for the question: who can know the future? Man does not know, only God knows. But as God created the art, so the art knows. Who taught the prophets how to speak? God alone. Who taught the arts? God alone also. But how can things be impossible for the art, but possible for God? Therefore, study without respite, so that the art may become perfect in us.

I. xii. 120-1

9.26

Magic transfers celestial forces to the medium in which such forces can operate. The medium is the centre, and the centre is man. Thus, through man, heavenly power may be brought into man so that in him is found the same action which is possible in the corresponding constellation. Thus man into whom magic has brought such forces becomes the star, with the star's secrets and arcana. Just as if somebody eats a herb, this herb is inside him with all its forces... If it is possible for poison or medicine with all its effects to be introduced into man by man, so the astronomer magus can imbue man with firmamental power... The magus learns only from the stars and not from man... Art is born with man, art and man are conceived together... The magus is not born of the natural stars but of the supernatural stars. Magic is impressed on the magus as is vision on the eyes and hearing on the ears—take the example of the magi of the past, none of whom was taught the book-learning of mortal man. For if a man goes to no other school but that which is made of bricks and mortar and seeks no other schoolmaster than one behind the stove, he will come to nothing except superficially. But the school of magic stands its test through Christ, who says 'Learn from me, for I am merciful and of a humble heart.'

I. xii. 122-4

9.27

The natural form of a tree is utterly familiar, but any plane can reduce it, so that the tree can no longer be recognized, and yet it is still the original wood. Cannot a sculptor also transform the original shape, while it remains the same material? Like-wise a painter. If Nature is able to achieve this through the coarse and clumsy elemental body, how much more can she achieve through the spiritual body, which is as subtle as sunshine? If the elemental body can make another form out of wood, the spiritual body can make from stone or wood another figure or form, which would astonish the elemental body. For the elemental body draws the art out of the spiritual body, but only receives the lesser values. The Master is superior to his disciples. Thus is follows that the Master of the Spirit can transform man just as a painter can change the figures in his picture. It is human *scientia* and not the stars which enable this, although the magus learns from the stars and is himself proficient.

I. xii. 125-6

9.28

One should not wonder at the additional species of characters and *gamaheu* [gems]. For if Nature is willing on her own account to endow herbs and stones with magical virtues, how much more can be achieved when she is induced to do so? For stones, herbs, and suchlike cannot be found in all places. Where does one find enough magnets? Or enough sapphires? When does one find everything in the leas and meadows? This lack compels the use of magic. Thus, Nature will put into words, *gamaheu*, and images virtues like those which inhere in herbs and roots... Cabbala also uses such magical forces... whatever the elemental body can achieve, the spiritual body can far surpass it by means of cabbalism... One should not be astonished by this, for the Scriptures say 'Ye are Gods'; we are much more like stars, only more powerful than them.

I. xii. 127-9

9.29

The difference between a saint and a magus is that the saint works through God, the magus through Nature.

I. xii. 130

9.30

A physician understands and knows all the virtues in the herbs. In the same way the magus understands what is in the stars, and nothing remains concealed in the heavens, which astronomy is able to interpret by means of its species. Now, the physician extracts the virtue from the herbs and calls this a remedy. The extract may have little weight, but it has many leas and meadows in its fist. But the extract alone is the remedy, not the leas and the meadows. Thus the magus can transfer many meadows of heaven into a small pebble which we call *gamaheu, imago,* or character. For these are boxes in which the magus keeps sidereal forces and virtues. Just as the physician can give his remedy to a patient and cure his disease, so the magus can transfer such virtues to man, after he has extracted them from the stars.

I. xii. 132-3

RELIGION AND POLITICS

10

LIBER PROLOGI IN VITAM BEATAM (1533)

10.1

Because a good tree bears good fruit and such a good tree grows from a good seed in the field, I am writing about the blessed life for those who represent the good tree or who strive towards it. For on one can be blessed after death unless they have been chosen to lead a blessed life on earth. If man must first be on earth, that which he wishes to be after death, he must strive towards it and think how he can attain this on earth. A bad seed produces a bad tree and in due course bad fruit, and a good seed produces a good tree and good fruit. But man is neither the good nor the bad seed. God is the good seed, the devil is the bad seed, and man is the field. If the good seed falls upon man, it will grow out of him. For man is the field, his heart is the tree, and his works are the fruit . . . The seed governs the field. The field is not master over the seed . . .

II. i. 69

10.2

When Christ and John the Baptist said 'Ye brood of vipers' to people, they meant a field that was good for nothing, in which no good could be seen, only snakes and vipers . . . Why is this? If man is inclined to evil, he receives the bad seed and bears the bad tree, and it is not possible for a good seed to fall upon him and to germinate. The bad seed smothers it. Then

God will not cast good seeds on this field, He will leave it barren and empty and overgrown with thistles. For one should note that man understands the difference between good and evil . . . God has made him responsible for knowing this and their respective consequences . . . This is the meaning of [the parable of the sower] when Christ said that some seed fell on good ground, some among thorns, and others on the rocks, and only those grew which had fallen on good ground. The good field recognizes good and evil in its conscience, knows the consequences, and rejects the evil in favour of the good . . . Whatever falls upon the field, falls according to the will of the field.

II. i. 70

10.3

Some like to claim that we have free will. This is not true. We do not choose, God chooses. God must give the evil to whoever does evil, otherwise he cannot do it. God must give the good to whoever does the good. How can a man do what he wants if he cannot even make a hair white or black? Who has free will, who can do what he likes with no one above him and no one to tell him otherwise? God alone. Who can say, 'I may stab someone or not stab him, I may steal or not steal, I may commit adultery or not, it is in my power alone'? No one can say this. Even if there were a thousand guilders before you and you wanted to take them, God could paralyse you, blind you, make you mad . . . But you are a field, you are free to accept what you want, good or evil. If you take the evil, the devil does it, not you. You may say, I did it of my own free will, but in fact the devil did it, it is his achievement. If you accept a good seed and revive the dead, heal lepers, drive devils out, you may not say, I can do it or not. You do not do it. God does it . . . If God is in you, you do God's works; if the devil is in you, you do his works . . . Man has no free will.

II. i. 71–2

10.4

I am writing about the blessed life not to teach the unfaithful or those ignorant of Christ, for I am no apostle nor anything like an apostle but a philosopher in the German manner. But I am writing for those who are baptized in Christ but who do not listen to Him, for those who set themselves above Christ, and for others who introduce many errors. I have things to tell these people and will demonstrate that things are not as they should be . . . If today's Christianity had prevailed at the time of Christ, one would have learnt that neither Christ nor St Peter would have allowed Catholic splendour but would have prevented it by atonement, prayer, and preaching. It is easy to see that things today are not as they were at the time of Christ. If Christ were to see the present violence of the Empire and the justice of all the kings, princes, lords, towns, and provinces, He would say this is not the law of God but the law of the devil . . . If Christ could see the trades and business of today, He would say this is usury and the work of the devil . . .

II. i. 76

10.5

The spirit bloweth where it listeth, not in everything, not in many things, but where it pleases. Many convince themselves that they themselves are the spirit, but the spirit has not been with them.

II. i. 78

10.6

To every existing thing God has allotted a time to grow in, lest it ripen prematurely. Much happens before it yields fruit: first come the buds, then the shoots, then the blossom, and then the fruits. But all are exposed to many accidents, many hazards, before they are harvested. Likewise with man: he has his goal in death, and death is the reaper of the human harvest, the vintner of his vineyard, the fruit-picker of his orchard. Birth is man's spring, when buds grow on his branches. Then come the shoots, then the blossoms, and finally the fruits. Should, then, the fruit of man—that is, his gift—be cut off when it is still a bud or a shoot? Man thinks, to be sure, that he is something, and because he bears more fruit than a nut tree, he thinks that there will always be more fruit in him. But this is not so. Man must be careful, for he does not bear the visible signs of the tree in the garden . . . For God gives no fruit before the appointed time; everything must come in due time. Some have an early harvest, some even earlier, others a late harvest, others even later . . . Before the flower is full-grown, no one should break forth with their wisdom, reason, and thoughts. For even the snakes are cautious and do not hatch before their time. It is God who makes you fly, with or without wings; He lets you imagine, think, judge. And when you think that you have flown as far as the third heaven, you have not even lifted yourself above the grass in the field and you are no use. You have smothered and burnt the fruit that was supposed to grow out of you, and now the fruit, together with you, has become worthless, for it has not prospered.

II. i. 78-9

10.7

What applies to pears and the fruit tree is even more applicable to man. Why does man want to fly before his fruits are ripe? They will not hide in you. If you have a vocation to write a book, you will not omit to do so, even if it is delayed for sixty or seventy years, or even longer. If you carry it in you and turn it over in your mind, you need not hurry it. It will not remain within, it will have to emerge, like a child from the belly of its mother. Whatever is born in this way is fertile and good, and then it never comes too late . . . Do not see the harvest in every thistle. I recall myself thinking I saw flowers in an alchemical process and then the fruit. But there was nothing. But there came a time when the fruit did appear. . . Whatever is in you must come forth, and you do not know how or whence it comes or whither it is going. And finally you will find in yourself something which you have never learned or seen.

II. i. 79-80

10.8

Blessed and more than blessed is the man to whom God gives the grace of poverty. But he who does not possess this grace thinks he is a rich man with much property, money and pleasure, and that he is mighty beside Emperor and Pope. But they are false Christians, they govern arrogantly, they have bad laws, they protect each other in their mischief, and you are abetting them and doing likewise following their laws and teachings. But it is the life of the devil . . . if you die thus, you will go to the devil. What do you want to do? If you leave your property to a monastery, it passes into the service of the devil . . . You should therefore sell everything and give [the proceeds] to the poor and embrace poverty . . . Become poor, as poor as a beggar, then the Pope will desert you, and the Emperor will desert you, and they will henceforth take you for a fool. But then you will have peace, and your folly will be great wisdom in the eyes of God. But if you are not ready to embrace voluntary poverty, you will walk away in sadness, like the youth whom Christ commanded to sell his house and land and follow Him.

II. i. 83

10.9

Therefore he who loves poverty is more than blessed. It frees him of many fetters and the prison of hell. He is not tempted towards usury, theft, murder, and so on. But he who loves riches sits on a shaky branch; a light breeze comes and he thinks of stealing, usury, speculating, and such things, which will help him to acquire the wealth of the devil and not that of God. Therefore let the doctrine of the blessed life be taught not to those who love riches, for they will find no pleasure in it, but only to those who delight in poverty and who wish to dwell in the community of the poor and in justice, so that no one may be above another in the satisfaction of his needs, but that each may suffer with the other, help him, and weep with him. For to rejoice with the merry and to grieve with the sad is fair and just.

II.i.83-4

10.10

He who wishes to be blessed on earth must found his teachings, his dominion, and his order upon the cornerstone of

Christ. It is from Christ that all things must be drawn. No doctrine avails unless it comes from heaven, no commandment
avails unless it comes from heaven, no art avails unless it comes
from heaven. And the same is true of all the rest . . . Man is
not master, God is master. We are not free but subjects. Our
freedom and our laws come from God and not from man.

II. i. 84–5

11

DE RELIGIONE PERPETUA
(1533)

11.1

Because God has created us and given each one of us a gift with which we can maintain ourselves on earth, He also commanded us to use this gift in a righteous way and not unrighteously. Although God has created great and wonderful things, of which we men can gain knowledge in many ways, and although He has given us great power to use them in many different ways, we are warned to use them only when we need them. For consider that a woman is created that she may give birth to children, yet not in disgrace, but only in honour. There are many great things created that they might be revealed to man through religion, one helping the other, but never otherwise than in the path of the Lord, not towards damnation, although all things can be employed for good as well as for evil purposes.

II. i. 89

11.2

All things that we use on earth, let us use them for good and not for evil. And never for more or for anything other than the purpose for which they exist. Add nothing, take nothing away, spoil nothing, and likewise better nothing.

II. i. 90

11.3

We have a religion known as apostleship. This religion was founded and ordained by God and consists of three parts: the Prophets, the Apostles, and the disciples. The Prophets are those who announced only what God had commanded. They are described in the Old Testament and proclaimed Christ, His teachings, and His sojourn on earth. In doing so they also held forth upon the God-willed path of righteousness. The last of these Prophets was John the Baptist, with whom the Old Testament ended and the New Testament began . . . Then came the Apostles. They proclaimed and preached the blessed life in Christ. They were twelve in number with their companions . . . Then they passed on. Thereupon came the disciples. They fulfil the proclamation of the Prophets and the apostolate of the Apostles . . . You should follow them because they show the blessed path in Christ to the blessed life. We should learn from them how we should walk on this path. For it is a religion which comes from God.

II. i. 90-1

11.4

God shows us these miracles by providing us with blessed people, who guide, lead and teach us in the eternal, blessed life. He has illuminated such people with the Holy Ghost, so that they speak in a wonderful way about the Kingdom of God and speak with great fiery tongues, so that one language understands many. That is the real reason for the holy teachers on earth, who take their doctrine from the Holy Ghost . . . There is the great truth before which all natural powers fall silent, and this truth lies in a single word. These doctrines of the disciples of Christ are to be trusted and believed. And they are never arrogant or rich but are (just) glad that their name is written in the book of the living. They may drink poison, but it harms them not; one can boil them in oil, but it harms them not. They can be lying in chains and will escape without the aid of men. They make the blind see, the lame straight, and all that they do they do for free, and they teach the word of God in a wonderful way for no reward. They disregard the riches of this world and wander without shoes, knapsack, or rod as a sign that their kingdom is not of this world. They walk in the footsteps of their master and Lord Christ . . . They are the salt in our heart, the light of this world and of all men. They come in the name of the Lord to tend and to give, to lead and to nourish. This is the veritable religion of the spirit which comes from heaven.

II. i. 91-2

11.5

These (disciples) are the truly poor. They nourish themselves just as the birds on the wing feed each day and give no thought for the morrow. They are as simple as doves but as clever as snakes in their office. They carry a burden in their office and leave nothing undone and complete all that is commanded of them. And when the hour of their death comes, they have completed their office with joy and die happy in the Lord and enter the everlasting life . . . They are pure in heart, they are chaste, they are gentle, they are merciful, they suffer and are patient for the sake of justice, they suffer much for the sake of Christ . . . They are not accursed like the Pharisees, the haughty, and the scribes, who appear handsome but are rogues and stinking bodies within. They do not teach of money, crops, or hay, but they speak of mercy, justice, and belief. They do not encourage external ornamentation but preach: improve yourselves, repent of your sins, believe in Christ and His teachings. Carry His yoke, it is light, carry His burden, it is small. They preach of the gentle, sweet Lord, who wants neither property nor money from His own, but a pure heart. We should follow them. We should love them. For we will thereby receive an eternal reward.

II. i. 92-3

11.6

Because God recognized from the beginning our susceptibility to many diseases, He knew in advance that we would not always have these disciples in the spirit of a true religion, but that they would be taken from us and others would come in their place . . . God has created and made a true religion for the benefit of the sick. This is medicine . . . and is no mean thing but second to the religion of the spirit. It is fitting that this (medicine) comes from God. For the evil enemy, whenever he can sow his seeds of discord, is intent on preventing the soul from having a vessel here on earth, and so he is pleased whenever a disaster befalls us. Thus he meddles in medicine in order that its truth cannot be established . . . This is very serious, for medicine is a part of religion and conducive to a blessed life among the people . . . For God does not will that we die, but that we live and repent of our sins and are sorry . . . Thus the wise man does not scorn medicine, for he knows it comes from God.

II. i. 94–5

11.7

The religion of the jurists should rest upon mercy and the path of forgiveness. For who can say what is right, and who among us mortals can presume to pass a judgement that will be valid before God, unless it has been inspired in him by the Holy Ghost and not out of a book or from his own imagination or his thoughts . . . Whoever is without sin, he may cast the first stone. How can anyone praise himself and condemn another, since no man knows who he is himself. Here lies the greatest error and contradiction in which the jurists are imprisoned. As long as they have been legislating and passing judgement, no one has ever been given his rights; the poor man comes off badly, the rich or clever man wins and not the slow-witted, the favoured and not the unfavoured. And all this happens according to the letter of the law. The letter sends the thief to the gallows, and the judge to eternal damnation. The true religion of the jurist should be to guide men to forgive, to pardon one another, to turn the other cheek. Not for nothing did God ordain it so.

II. i. 103–4

11.8

Because we know that our kingdom is not of this earth, we need no more than enough food and clothing, and we cannot take it with us [when we die] . . . We should enrich ourselves in works and virtues, which will follow us into the next world. Even if we have the favour of all princes and kings and are held in high esteem by them, if the Highest King does not approve, what are all the kings on earth worth? Therefore: do not seek to please men, seek to please God; do not be rich in earthly things but in heavenly things; do not be learned in profane things but in sacred things; and use our whole religion that we may pass in joy from this earth in our eternal body to the eternal life, and stand happily and unafraid before God the Almighty with our religions. For our works, the products of the gifts which God gave us, will follow us to Heaven. And the works which we did outside those gifts will follow us into eternal damnation. For each of us will be tested before the Highest.

II. i. 107

12

DE HONESTIS UTRISQUE DIVITIIS (1533)

12.1

Happy are all those who fear the Lord and follow in His paths. If one is to describe honourable right livelihood, the first steps towards it must be taken from the word of the eternal God . . . We ourselves cannot devise and apprehend right livelihood, which is divine and pleasing to God. For our reason, wisdom, and all our knowledge cannot understand this. Everyone would just create a livelihood which seemed right in his own eyes, but it might be theft in God's eyes. For God wants us all to help each other and live in such a way that no one is guilty of acting against his neighbour or making a living contrary to the divine life. This blessed way of making a living derives from God, our Maker . . . and David begins to describe this right livelihood (Psalm 128), saying: Happy are all those who fear the Lord and follow in His paths . . . We should nourish ourselves, fearing God and following in His paths. That is right livelihood.

II. i. 241

12.2

You will nourish yourself by the work of your own hands. If right livelihood lies solely in work and not in sloth, then all means of livelihood not gained by work are to be rejected and excluded from the paths of righteousness. But what is the right work of one's own hands? One which benefits and does not harm your neighbour. How? If you are a physician, your hand is the art and you nourish yourself by it. But you should make a living from your patients in such a way that their own livelihood is not diminished. For they maintain themselves with many kinds of manual work, helping you and helping their neighbour, and in neither case accumulating wealth. You could accumulate riches by practising as a physician, but then your virtue would be in vain. He who serves the altar can claim his share from the altar (I Cor. 9: 13). The altar is your hand. Livelihood does not consist in riches but only in our needs. For needs are a form of love, because they are not directed towards riches. Wealth takes advantage of one's neighbour ... You should maintain yourself but not in wealth—that is damnation; in poverty there is happiness. For our kingdom is not of this world, but of the one to come.

II. i. 241-2

12.3

Although you may be able to produce a ton of gold, consider that you cannot consume a ton, it is too much for you. For death can take you tomorrow and you will be no more, but your ton is still there. What good is it if you earn a great deal by your 'hand'—whether by your brain, feet, tongue, eyes, or genitals—enrich yourself and are happy in the world, but not in God's eyes? Use your limbs to satisfy your needs in which God will not forsake you. Why do you need any more, when you cannot keep it? You may be a farmer and have many fields, many estates and enjoy them—what is this pleasure? You do not eat everything; give your helpers their livelihood, give half to the needy, pile up no treasure, which the worms, flies, and moths eat. It is sufficient that each day brings its own trouble, cares, and need. That is no cross to bear. But worrying about tomorrow is a cross to bear. For we should not be burdened with care nor concerned with anything beyond necessities. As God provides for the birds—for their livelihood not their wealth—so will He provide for us. If you are a merchant, what does it amount to if you invest so well that you become a king?

What is your kingdom with regard to happiness? Nothing but damnation results from your riches. If you are a merchant, consider that your purchase is a livelihood to your neighbour. Before you sell, subtract your profit, so that you offer a just purchase and so that death will not find you wealthy. Happy are those who die in the Lord. They are the poor who have not sought debauchery here on earth.

II. i. 242-3

12.4

Happiness and prosperity will be yours. If you are one who does not accumulate riches but works for his needs, then you are happy and you will prosper. This is because you are not stealing. For theft occurs on account of riches, whenever one makes a living without working. Nor are you killing. For it is akin to killing when you procure the property of another or cause another to procure it for a mere wage . . . Thou shalt not kill. For one kills if one makes a living other than by one's own hand. Now there are two types of killing: killing out of envy or anger with neither enrichment nor profit; and killing for profit. Killing without profit is not our concern. Here we consider killing for a livelihood. There are two types of such killing: one may murder, take the property of the victim, and live on it; and there is the 'public' killing of another for the sake of one's own livelihood. This kind of 'killing' is also twofold: just and unjust. It is just if you are content with your wage which represents no more than right livelihood. [But there are those who] realize their desire for the property of another . . . Then you are making your living by killing, strangling, and wars—not only killing a man but strangling his beasts, burning his house, so that everything dies . . . If you kill the beast of another man, you eat it and use it for your own ends and nourishment. Then you are but a thief and a robber and not living justly. And if you take the beast and give it to another, then you are a thief, an abettor of murder, and a traitor. For you are stealing from your neighbour what is his and betraying it to another . . . If this man takes the beast to the butcher, which is meet and right but only for him who has worked for it, such blood must cry to God, because the blood of the just does cry to God, and your murderous blood does not. Because God passes judgement on all those who break His commandment with respect to their neighbour and you are breaking this protection for the sake of your own livelihood, which does not arise from need but from superfluous riches, nor gain from the work of your own hand but a luxury contrary to the mercy and gift of God. If you cut another's corn or use his hay, you are killing what is his. For you are eating and killing him on his field. It is no sin to kill what one has planted; it is a sin and murder when one has not grown it but cuts it down ... Therefore if you want to lead a righteous life, make your living by the work of your own hands.

II. i. 246-9

12.5

In order that we mortal men might become immortal, God gave us our eternal body and showed us right livelihood that we might not lose it: to nourish ourselves by our own work and to renounce all sloth. And He gave us a commandment: thou shalt not steal. What else is stealing but making a living without work, or doing more than one's needs require? ... Work is nothing but the sweat of our body and not sparing it. Whatever livelihood involves no sweat is contrary to the righteous life. This is evident in theft. What does it signify, to take nothing from another? To take nothing of his work. We should not eat the sweat of another, we should not eat the work of his hand but of our own hand, giving like for like. Now each pays the other: the furrier the winter coat, the tailor the summer dress; thus the carpenter the mason and vice versa ... God has ordained that every man's work shall pay him. For sweat pays sweat, work pays work, and sloth pays nothing. To nourish oneself without sweat is to nourish oneself by theft. For sloth is contrary to works, and without works there is no nourishment.

II. i. 249-50

12.6

But there is yet another livelihood of sloth which is contrary to the teaching of God. Whenever you lend money against interest, and you consume the interest without touching the capital—what besides theft can that be compared with? The reason: you are eating the sweat of another. But you should eat your own sweat and not anyone else's. What sweat of your brow do you shed in earning interest on money with no reduction in capital. You are at leisure. Lend, not to eat, but to help another. That is pleasing to God. For you should work yourself, nourish yourself, not have another nourish you. In order that you should nourish yourself, God made you strong, powerful, with healthy limbs, keen, and agile ... That is why He gave you a gift [talent] with which you should nourish yourself. Do not bury it in the earth. Learn it, use it. For God created neither you nor any man for idleness but for work.

II. i. 251-2

12.7

You should feed yourself by the sweat of your brow. You should eat the work of your own hands and thus you will be happy ... But all those who do not work will be disregarded, thus spake the Prophet. Those who eat the work of their hands are blessed, but those who do not eat their own handiwork are accursed. Because the eternal life is lost by such accursed livelihood, no father should leave wealth to his children so that they can indulge in indolence, but should leave them the farm, the work, the business itself ... One should not let interest, ground-rents, tithes, and revenues accrue and allow another to indulge in indolence. God does not walk in these paths nor command us to do so ... For happiness is not in rest, not in debauchery, not in riches, not in the mouth, not in the belly, but in work and in sweat ...

II. i. 253

12.8

Be righteous and you will prosper. The enemy on earth who tempts us is clever and painstaking at diverting us from the paths of God into the path of wealth. He ponders and thinks day and night how he can drive our sweat towards riches and self-interest. For instance, he says to the peasants: keep the

product of your work, give nothing away for free, and accumulate a fortune; buy more than the next man, make your wealth
grow, and eventually your children will be idlers, noblemen,
estate-owners, and burghers. And this is not only possible for
peasants but with all gifts. Anyone with a gift can deploy it
for riches, thereby forgetting neighbourly love and the fact that
riches serve damnation and are a diversion from God. God gave
us gifts for our livelihood and for each to help the other in his
need. He gave the Saints power to heal the sick, to make the
blind see, and to revive the dead. But He did not intend that
riches should result from such power and gifts. [Wealth] is a
diversion from God and a disgrace to the gifts of God
. . . Everyone has a gift which he should use for his neighbour's
benefit, and his neighbour can do likewise: thus you should
build houses for others, not just your own; sow corn for others,
not just for your own mouth; and plant vines for others, not
just for your own gizzard. The earth belongs to all men, to
no one more than any other.

II. i. 254-5

13

DE ORDINE DONI (1533)

13.1

To us on earth God has given gifts and virtues, which each may and should use in the service of others, not for himself. One should therefore consider how each gift is to be used with regard to one's neighbour, in order that the commandment of God be fulfilled. Although Satan has often violently hindered this neighbourly love and directed us towards self-interest, he can achieve nothing if we walk in the paths of God and strive to fulfil the will of God . . . Thus there follows an order of the gifts of each one of us with regard to our neighbour . . . There are four gifts on earth: agriculture, crafts, the creative arts, and authority. They all maintain one another, and each one uses and supports the other three and vice versa. These four are so closely linked that no one can reject the others and isolate itself. No one could say to the other, what do I care about you, I have my own gift for myself alone; so that the creative artists might say, create your own art; the authorities, protect yourselves. Agriculture has two elements: those who own the land and those who work it. They must work it because they have nothing themselves but are servants, and the landlords cannot work it by themselves. But the servants should not be kept like beasts . . . For he who serves the altar can claim his share from the altar and the gift which God has given us. The man who owns the land should not work, provided that he who does not own the land may nevertheless enjoy the land. For he gains this through his work ... To conclude: there is no monarchia without its master and servant. The gift of the master and the gift of working for the servant ...

II. ii. 51-4

13.2

But although they may have servants, the masters are not idle ... each master works by ensuring that his servant does his job properly, forgets nothing, and leaves nothing incomplete. The master-craftsman should not practise his craft single-handed but should eat the work of his servant and vice versa. The worries of interest payments and securities are the work of the master ... And as can be observed in any craft, masters have special gifts which servants do not possess ... A master should work on a task where he is more productive than his servant; whenever this is not the case, he should let the servant do the work ... Therefore he should leave the common work to his servant and work on the subtle tasks. For there is no craft on earth which does not have its advanced problems. In this way the master receives instruction by giving up the common work to the servant. The discovery of many subtle things would be hindered by the master's having to perform servile tasks. These discoveries are more than simple work ... If you are a scholar, you do not do everything alone; you let others copy, bind, illuminate, while you think more profoundly. For what good is it if you can replace ten servants and thereby save their wages and bread? It will all pass with your death. But the contrary is rightful in God's eyes. Like a farmer who has a great deal of land and cannot look after it by himself. Servants come to work, clothe themselves, eat, and drink from its produce as well as the farmer. There is even a surplus.

II. ii. 54-6

13.3

The authorities should also provide the servants with jobs. For Christ did not want to do everything on his own, but needed apostles. The Emperor, even if he could do everything alone, should not only take representatives but those who have full authority. Who knows—if they live in the fear of God—these governors might be more gifted that the Emperor himself . . . For he who was cured by St Peter is just as healthy as he who has been cured by Christ. The disciple is like the master; whoever does not accept the disciple rejects the master—and if he were to fly to the master, he would not listen to him. For God does not work to be scorned in his Saints. Nor the Emperor in his sergeants. For all this is done through servants, just as God sent the angel Gabriel to Mary. That is how God wants it . . . God could easily give us food and drink in the rain without our having to work, but he wants the earth to give its product through work, nothing without a means.

II. ii. 56-7

13.4

In order to avoid self-interest, the subjection of the poor, and the profiteering of the rich, it is necessary that each be master of one and not numerous things. For example, there are a thousand peasants with their servants. Now there is a disaster, in that the snow freezes the seeds in one place but not in another . . . In one place there is abundance, in another poverty. Now love demands an order so that one part helps the other to bear its cross . . . The same applies to the crafts . . . Each has his special gift, art, wisdom, righteousness. Whoever is more and a superior, he is a yet greater servant and he should be all the more subordinate without any envy and disloyalty. No one should think otherwise than: if my neighbour had more than I, a good order would result. Thus agriculture is the first order, for whoever is affected by hail is in the same position as he who is not affected. This applies to wine, corn, oats, hay, poultry, cattle; each part can benefit from the other, if they need to.

II. ii. 57-8

13.5

The authorities should help to establish this neighbourly love and ensure that everyone does not do as they like. The Scriptures say: force him to go in. Take an example from viniculture. A particularly fine grape is planted throughout the country. After it has been harvested and lies in barrels, a tax is levied, and with its proceeds new planting can begin. Thus, those who have done well and those who have not done well receive the same, and each is maintained in their work. Whoever has much comes to the aid of him who has nothing . . . Thus by means of a simple way we will be fed by our Heavenly Father. But self-interest has continual worries over loss, whereas a communal love does not.

II. ii. 58-60

13.6

There needs to be a different attitude and comparison with the crafts: one man has many children but less work and custom; the other has fewer or no children and much custom. Here love and brotherhood must be upheld . . . It is real brotherhood when all craftsmen benefit alike. For example, all the cobblers, those with and those without custom, have to work. And when all the shoes are made for the children, women, men, masters, and servants . . . the total cost is reckoned up and divided by the total number of shoes and they are sold at this price—then the rich cobbler is working for the poor cobbler.

II. ii. 60-1

13.7

Self-interest makes mendacious people out of you noblemen and authorities. Your food and needs are provided by the three other 'monarchies'. You owe money to nobody for anything in the three monarchies, neither to the cobbler nor to the tailor . . . In order to cover your needs you must buy corn, meat, and salt for money and so you raise taxes . . . Buying increases, prices rise, and cereals and bread are dearer . . . But you can prevent this by not settling with money but with that which the money is supposed to buy, namely with corn, meat, salt, and bread. How much milder and better you would govern if you were rid of money. For wherever there is money, there is worry. That is what causes murders; bread and meat do not

cause them. You become profiteers, gamblers, debauchees, and
whores from money, and your money does no one any good.
You do not invest it in the country but give it to the whores
and the Pharisees, and there is only bad feeling, dishonour, mischief, and evil, wealth, dancing, tournaments, and banqueting.
These represent no virtue on the part of the authorities. But
seek your triumph in the wisdom of doing what is sufficient,
the virtue of justice and truth.

II. ii. 63-4

13.8

Outside the four monarchies there is yet another livelihood
created by God—namely the hunting of birds, fish, and wild
animals. No one but God feeds them, but they come to us and
nourish us. Therefore this livelihood shall belong to the poor,
because it is superfluous to the hierarchy of masters and servants: the poor folk may learn how to fish, catch birds, and
hunt wild animals in the woods and the fields . . . Thus, you
outside the four monarchies, support yourselves in a communal
'landscape', each concerned with the other and not with himself. Thus God gives us peace, rest, health, and food in many
ways with much joy among neighbours, parents and children,
strangers and local people. But if we do not act in this way,
there is plague, inflation, hunger, war, wrangling, and strife,
and each is against all. And neither the sun nor the moon is
favourable to us and none to another, [even] the beasts on the
road hate us. Such is the reign of the devil.

II. ii. 64-5

13.9

There are several gangs outside the monarchies which make
a living on the paths of unrighteousness, such as the merchants,
interest brokers, money-lenders, buying agents, rag-and-bone
men, hucksters, and many others, who all make a living out
of the other four [monarchies], neither as masters nor as servants. They have an alien ungodly livelihood which is forbid-
den in the Ten Commandments. Lending money and earning
interest destroys commonality. Agency creates inflation and

comes from the devil and his own. For these people behave
like false prophets towards the common man. They talk gli-
bly, and the common man knows no better. Satan draws his
authority from them . . . You will know them by their works.
They lie and trick, lend on interest, against security . . . why
do you tolerate them among you? You may think they are on
your side, but they are only on their own side and respect
neither God nor His kingdom. They take the highest chair and
the highest place at the table, and the whole world defers to
them.

II. ii. 65–6

13.10

They call a disgrace a clever move, a deception a masterpiece.
There can be no greater deception of one's neighbour than the
doings of businessmen. Their whole life is devilish. They seduce
rich and poor . . . They steal the land and labour from princes
and lords with cunning and polite deception. They seduce all
estates and want to be the best, they are the greatest favourites
of the princes and are held in high regard. They mix with the
nobility and the princes only to swindle them hugely . . . What
is their luxury, what is their belief, what is their whole Christian life? Nothing, for it is all deception and a devilish life. They
are pepper-traders and deal in spices. What good is it? Whom
does it benefit? . . . Does not a peasant live as well on turnips
as someone who eats spices? All traders in spices are full of
the devil and his servants, through whom he disgraces the people . . . They are whores and rogues, thieves and scoundrels
. . . Where does their wealth come from? From lies, deceptions,
and unjust takings.

II. ii. 66–7

13.11

Then there are the merchants' hirelings, the factors and the
bookkeepers. Look what kind of people they are . . . They cannot eat, drink, and whore enough, tempting youth with all their
tricks, inventing all sorts of rubbish and luxury. It all comes
from idleness. What is the use of their services to the poor and

the faithful? Is there any honesty, courage, or justice in them?
They have all the power in the town and the country. Whoever
has no wealth, has no honour and is worthless in their league.
Thus the poor man is swindled out of his standards and his
trust and picks up their attitudes and learns to deceive in order
not to lose face ... The cleverer a businessman, the greater
his deceit.

II. ii. 68

PANSOPHY, MAGIC AND CABBALA

DE NATURA RERUM (1537)

14.1

BOOK I
CONCERNING THE GENERATION OF
NATURAL THINGS

The generation of all natural things is twofold: one which takes place by Nature without Art, the other which is brought about by Art, that is to say, by Alchemy, though, generally, it might be said that all things are generated from the earth by the help of putrefaction. For putrefaction is the highest grade, and the first initiative to generation. But putrefaction originates from a moist heat. For a constant moist heat produces putrefaction and transmutes all natural things from their first form and essence, as well as their force and virtue, into something else. For as putrefaction in the bowels transmutes and reduces all foods into dung, so, also, without the belly, putrefaction in glass transmutes all things from one form to another, from one essence to another, from one colour to another, from one odour to another, from one virtue to another, from one force to another, from one set of properties to another, and, in a word, from one quality to another. For it is known and proved by daily experience that many good things which are healthful and a medicine, become, after their putrefaction, bad, unwholesome, and mere poison. So, on the other hand, many things are bad, unwholesome, poisonous, and hurtful, which after their putrefaction become good, lose all their evil effect, and make noble medicines. For putrefaction brings forth great effects, as we have a good example in the sacred gospel, where Christ says, 'Unless a grain of wheat be cast forth into a field and putrefy, it cannot bear fruit a hundred fold.' Hence it may be known that many things are multiplied by putrefaction so that they produce excellent fruit. For putrefaction is the change and death of all things, and the destruction of the first essence of all natural objects, from whence there issues forth for us regeneration and a new birth ten thousand times better than before.

Since, then, putrefaction is the first step and commencement of generation, it is in the highest degree necessary that we should thoroughly understand this process. But there are many kinds of putrefaction, and one produces its generation better than another, one more quickly than another. We have also said that what is moist and warm constitutes the first grade and the beginning of putrefaction, which procreates all things as a hen procreates her eggs. Wherefore by and in putrefaction everything becomes mucilaginous phlegm and living matter, whatever it eventually turns out to be. You see an example in eggs, wherein is mucilaginous moisture, which by continuous heat putrefies and is quickened into the living chicken, not only by the heat which comes from the hen, but by any similar heat. For by such a degree of heat eggs can be brought to maturity in glass, and by the heat of ashes, so that they become living birds. Any man, too, can bring the egg to maturity under his own arm and procreate the chicken as well as the hen. And here something more is to be noticed. If the living bird be burned to dust and ashes in a sealed cucurbite with the third degree of fire, and then, still shut up, be putrefied with the highest degree of putrefaction in a *venter equinus* so as to become a mucilaginous phlegm, then that phlegm can again be brought to maturity, and so, renovated and restored, can become a living bird, provided the phlegm be once more enclosed in its jar or receptacle. This is to revive the dead by regeneration and clarification, which is indeed a great and profound miracle of Nature. By this process all birds can be killed and again made to live, to be renovated and restored. This is the very greatest and highest miracle and mystery of God, which God has disclosed to mortal man. For you must know that in this way men can be generated without natural father and mother; that is to say, not in the natural way from the woman, but by the art and industry of a skilled Spagyrist a man can be born and grow, as will hereafter be described.

I. xi. 312-13

14.2

But neither must we by any means forget the generation of homunculi. For there is some truth in this thing, although for a long time it was held in a most occult manner and with secrecy, while there was no little doubt and question among some of the old Philosophers, whether it was possible to Nature and Art, that a man should be begotten without the female body and the natural womb. I answer hereto, that this is in no way opposed to Spagyric Art and to Nature, nay, that it is perfectly possible. In order to accomplish it, you must proceed thus. Let the semen of a man putrefy by itself in a sealed cucurbite with the highest putrefaction of the *venter equinus* for forty days, or until it begins at last to live, move, and be agitated, which can easily be seen. After this time it will be in some degree like a human being, but, nevertheless, transparent and without body. If now, after this, it be every day nourished and fed cautiously and prudently with the arcanum of human blood, and kept for forty weeks in the perpetual and equal heat of a *venter equinus*, it becomes, thenceforth, a true and and living infant, having all the members of a child that is born from a woman, but much smaller. This we call a homunculus; and it should be afterwards educated with the greatest care and zeal, until it grows up and begins to display intelligence. Now, this is one of the greatest secrets which God has revealed to mortal and fallible man. It is a miracle and marvel of God, an arcanum above all arcana, and deserves to be kept secret until the last times, when there shall be nothing hidden, but all things shall be made manifest.

I. xi. 316-17

14.3

Here, too, it would be necessary to speak about the generation of metals, but since we have written sufficiently of these in our book *The Generation of Metals*, we will treat the matter very briefly here, and only in a short space point out what we there omitted. Know, then, that all the seven metals are born from a threefold matter, namely, Mercury, Sulphur, and Salt, but with distinct and peculiar colourings. In this way, Hermes truly said that all the seven metals were made and compounded of three substances, and in like manner also tinctures and the Philosophers' Stone. These three substances he names Spirit, Soul, and Body. But he did not point out how this was to be understood, or what he meant by it, though possibly he might also have known the three principles, but he makes no mention of them. I do not therefore say that he was in error, but that he was silent. Now, in order that these three distinct substances may be rightly understood, namely, spirit, soul, and body, it should be known that they signify nothing else than the three principles, Mercury, Sulphur, and Salt, from which all the seven metals are generated. For Mercury is the spirit, Sulphur is the soul, and Salt is the body. The metal between the spirit and the body, concerning which Hermes speaks, is the soul, which indeed is Sulphur. It unites those two contraries, the body and the spirit, and changes them into one essence. But it must not be understood that from any Mercury, and any Sulphur, and any Salt, these seven metals can be generated, or, in like manner, the Tincture or the Philosophers' Stone by the Art and the industry of the Alchemist in the fire; but all these seven metals must be generated in the mountains by the *Archeus* of the earth. The alchemist will more easily transmute metals than generate or make them. Nevertheless, live Mercury is the mother of all the seven metals, and deserves to be called the Mother of Metals.

I. xi. 318

14.4

BOOK II
CONCERNING THE GROWTH OF NATURAL THINGS

It is clear enough, and well known to everybody, that all natural things grow and mature by warmth and moisture, as is plainly demonstrated by the rain followed up with sunshine. None can deny that the earth is rendered fruitful by the rain, and all must confess that every kind of fruit is ripened by the sun. Since, then, by the Divine institution, this is possible to Nature, who will deny or refuse to believe that man possesses this same power by a prudent and skilful pursuit of the Alchemical Art, so that he shall render the fruitless fruitful, the unripe ripe, and make all increase and grow? The Scripture says that God subjected all created things to man, and handed them over to him as if they were his own property, so that he might use them for his necessity, that he might have dominion over the fishes of the sea, the fowls of the air, and everything on the earth without exception. Wherefore man ought to rejoice because God has illuminated him and endowed him, so that all God's creatures are compelled to obey Him and to be subject to Him, especially all the earth, together with all things which are born, live, and move in it and upon it. Since, then, we see with our eyes, and are taught by daily experience, that the oftener and the more plentifully the rain moistens the earth, and the sun dries it again with its heat and glow, the sooner the fruits of the earth come forth and ripen, while all fruits increase and grow, whatever be the time of year, let none wonder that the alchemist, too, by manifold imbibitions and distillations, can produce the same effect. For what is rain but the imbibition of the earth? What are the heat and glow of the sun other than the sun's process of distillation, which again extracts the humidity? Wherefore I say that it is possible by such co-optation in the middle of winter to produce green herbs, flowers, and fruits, by means of earth and water, from seed and root. Now, if this takes place with herbs and flowers, it will take place in many other similar things too, as, for instance, in all minerals, the imperfect metals whereof can be ripened with mineral water by the industry and art of the skilled alchemist. So, too, can all marcasites, granites, zincs, arsenics, talcs, cachimiae, bismuths, antimonies, etc., all of which carry with them immature Sol and Luna, be so ripened as to be made equal to the richest veins of gold and silver, only by such co-optation. So, also, the Elixir and Tinctures of metals are matured and perfected.

I. xi. 320-1

14.5

It is also possible for gold to be so acted upon by the industry and art of the skilled alchemist that it will grow in a cucurbite with many wonderful branches and leaves, which experiment is very pleasant to behold, and full of marvels. The process is as follows. Let gold be calcined by means of aqua regis so that it becomes a chalky lime; which place in a cucurbite, pouring in good and fresh aqua regis and water of graduation so that it exceeds four fingers across. Extract it again with the third degree of fire until nothing more ascends. Again pour over it distilled water, and once more extract by distillation as before. Do this until you see the Sol rise in the glass and grow in the form of a tree with many branches and leaves. Thus there is produced from Sol a wonderful and beautiful shrub which alchemists call the Golden Herb, or the Philosophers' Tree. The process is the same with the other metals, save that the calcination may be different, and some other aqua fortis may have to be used. This I leave to your experience. If you are practised in Alchemy you will do what is right in these details.

I. xi. 322

14.6

BOOK IV
CONCERNING THE LIFE OF NATURAL THINGS

None can deny that the air gives life to all corporeal and substantial things which are born and generated from the earth. But as to what and of what kind the life of each particular thing is, it should be known that the life of things is none other than a spiritual essence, an invisible and impalpable thing, a spirit and a spiritual thing. On this account there is nothing corporeal but has latent within itself a spirit and life, which, as just now said, is none other than a spiritual thing. But not only that lives which moves and acts, as men, animals, worms in the earth, birds under the sky, fishes in the sea, but also all corporeal and substantial things. For here we should know that God, at the beginning of the creation of all things, created no body whatever without its own spirit, which spirit it contains after an occult manner within itself. For what is the body without the spirit?

Absolutely nothing. So it is that the spirit holds concealed within itself the virtue and power of the thing, and not the body. For in the body is death, and the body is subject to death, and in the body nothing but death must be looked for. For the body can be destroyed and corrupted in various ways, but not the spirit: for it always remains a living spirit, and is bound up with life. It also keeps its own body alive, but in the removal of the body from it, it leaves the body separate and dead, and returns to its own place whence it had come, that is to say, into chaos, and into the air of the higher and lower firmament. Hence it is evident that there are different kinds of spirits, just as there are different kinds of bodies. There are celestial and infernal spirits, human and metallic, the spirits of salts, gems, and marcasites, arsenical spirits, spirits of potables, of roots, of liquids, of flesh, blood, bones, etc. Wherefore you may know that the spirit is in very truth the life and balsam of all corporeal things. Now we will go on to its species, and here will describe to you in detail, but as briefly as possible, the life of each natural thing.

The life, then, of all men is none other than a certain astral balsam, a balsamic impression, a celestial and invisible fire, an included air, and a spirit of salt which tinges. I am unable to name it more clearly, although it could be put forward under many distinctive titles. Since, however, the chief and the best are here pointed out, we will be silent as to the rest and the inferior names.

The life of metals is a latent fatness which they have received from Sulphur. This is shown from their fluxion, because everything which passes into flux in the fire does so on account of its hidden fatness. Unless this were so no metal could be reduced to a fluid state, as we see in the case of iron and steel, which have the least Sulphur and fatness of all the metals, wherefore they are of a drier nature than all the rest of them.

The life of Mercury is nothing but inner heat and outer frigidity. That is to say, within it gives heat, but without it causes cold; and in this respect it is aptly to be compared to a garment of skins, which, like Mercury, causes both heat and cold. For if a garment of this kind be worn by a man, it warms him and protects him from the cold; but if he wears the hairless part against his naked body, it causes cold, and defends him from excessive heat. So it came about that in very ancient times, and it is even the custom still, that these coats of skin are worn both in summer and in winter, as much against the heat as against the cold; in summer the hairless part is turned within, and the hairy part outside, but in the cold winter season the hairy part is turned within and the hairless part outside. As it is with the garment of skins, so is it with Mercury.

I. xi. 329-331

14.7

The life of Sulphur is a combustible, ill-smelling fatness. Whilst it flames and sends forth its evil odour it may be said to live.

The life of all salts is nothing else but a spirit of aqua fortis: for when the water is abstracted from them, that which remains at the bottom is called dead earth.

The life of gems and corals is mere colour, which can be taken from them by spirits of wine. The life of pearls is their bright-ness, which they lose in their calcination. The life of the mag-net is the spirit of iron, which can be extracted and taken away by rectified *vinum ardens* itself, or by spirit of wine.

The life of flints is a mucilaginous matter. The life of mar-casites, cachymiae, talc, cobalt, zinc, granites, zwitter, vismat [rude tin], is a metallic spirit of antimony, which has the power to tinge. Of arsenicals, auripigment, orpiment, realgar, and simi-lar matters, the life is a mineral coagulated poison.

The life of wavelike substances, that is to say, of the dung of men and animals, is their strong and foetid smell. When this is lost they are dead.

The life of aromatic substances, to wit, musk, ambergris, civet, and whatever emits a strong, sweet, and pleasant odour, is nothing but that grateful odour itself. If they lose this they are dead and useless.

The life of sweet things, as sugar, honey, manna, fistula cas-siae, and the like, is a subtle sweetness, with the power to tinge; for if that sweetness be taken away by distillation, or sublima-tion, the things are dead, fatuous, and no longer of any value.

The life of resins, as caraba, turpentine, and gum, is a mucilaginous, glittering fatness. They all give excellent varnish; when they no longer furnish this, and lose their glitter, they are dead.

The life of herbs, roots, apples, and other fruits of this kind, is nothing else than the liquid of the earth, which they spontaneously lose if they are deprived of water and earth.

The life of wood is a certain resin. Any wood that is deprived of resin is unable longer to flourish.

The life of bones is the liquid of *mumia*. The life of flesh and blood is none other than the spirit of Salt, which preserves them from ill odour and decay, and spontaneously, as the water is separated from them.

But concerning the life of the elements there is this to be known. The life of water is its flowing. When it is coagulated by the cold of the firmament and congealed into ice, then it is dead, and all power of doing harm is taken from it, since no one can any longer be drowned in it.

So, too, the life of fire is air, for the air makes the fire blaze more strongly and with greater impetuosity. Some air proceeds from all fire, sufficient to extinguish a candle or to lift a light feather, as is evident to the eyes. All live fire, therefore, if it be shut up or deprived of the power to send forth its air, must be suffocated.

The air lives of itself, and gives life to all other things. The earth, however, is of itself dead; but its own element is its invisible and occult life.

I. xi. 331-2

14.8

BOOK V
CONCERNING THE DEATH OF NATURAL THINGS

The death of all natural things is nothing else but an alteration and removal of their powers and virtues, an overthrow of their potencies for evil or for good, an overwhelming and blotting out of their former nature, and the generation of a new and different nature. For it should be known that many things which in life were good, and had their own virtues, retain little or none of that virtue when they are dead, but appear altogether

fatuous and powerless. So, on the other hand, many things in
their life are evil, but in death, or after they have been mortified, they display a manifold power and efficacy, and do much
good. We could recount many examples of this, but that is
altogether foreign to our purpose. Yet, in order that you may
see that I do not write from my mere opinion, however plau-
sible, but from my experience, it is well that I should adduce
one example with which I will quiet and silence the sophists
who say that nothing can be gained from dead things, nor anything ought to be sought or found in them. The cause of this
assertion is that they value at nothing the preparations of the
alchemists, by which many great secrets of this kind are discovered. For look at Mercury, live and crude Sulphur, and crude
antimony; as they are brought from the mines, that is, while
they are still living, how small is their virtue, how lightly and
tardily do they exercise their influence. Indeed, they bring more
evil than good, and are rather a poison than a medicine. But
if, by the industry of a skilled alchemist, they are corrupted
into their first substance and prudently prepared (that is, if the
Mercury be coagulated, precipitated, sublimated, resolved, and
turned into oil; the Sulphur be sublimated, calcined, reverberated and turned into oil; and, in like manner, Venus be sublimated, calcined, reverberated, and turned into oil), you see what
usefulness, what power and virtue, and what rapid efficiency
they afford and display, so that none can fully speak or write
of it. For their manifold virtues are not to be investigated, nor
can anyone search them out. Every alchemist, therefore, and
every faithful physician, ought to seek into these three things
during his whole life, and even up to his death should play with
them and find his pastime in them. Most assuredly they will
nobly compensate him for all his labour, study, and expense.

I. xi. 332-3

14.9

BOOK VI
CONCERNING THE RESUSCITATION OF
NATURAL THINGS

The resuscitation and reduction of natural things is not the least important in the nature of things, but a profound and great secret, rather divine and angelic than human and natural. I would, however, on this point be understood with the greatest discrimination, and in no other way than according to my fixed opinion, as Nature daily and clearly points out and experience proves; so that I may not be exposed to the lies and misrepresentations of my enemies the quack doctors (by whom I am constantly ill-judged), as if I myself pretend to usurp some divine power, or to attribute that same to Nature which she never claims. Therefore, at this point, the most careful observation is necessary, since death is twofold, that is to say, violent or spontaneous. From the one, a thing can be resuscitated, but not from the other. Do not, then, believe the sophists when they tell you that a thing once dead or mortified cannot be resuscitated, and when they make light of resuscitation and restoration; for their mistake is great. It is indeed true that whatever perishes by its own natural death, or whatever mortifies by Nature according to its own predestination, God alone can resuscitate, or that it must be done by His divine command. So whatever Nature consumes man cannot restore. But whatever man destroys man can restore, and break again when restored. Beyond this man by his condition has no power, and if anyone strove to do more he would be arrogating to himself the power of God, and yet would labour in vain and be confounded, unless God were with him, or he had such faith that he could remove mountains. To such a man this, and still greater things, would be possible, since Scripture says, for Christ Himself had said—'If ye have faith as a grain of mustard-seed, and say to this mountain: Depart and place yourself yonder, it would do so and place itself there; and all things shall be possible, and nothing impossible, to you.'

But let us return to our proposition. What is the difference between dying and being mortified, and from which of these conditions is resuscitation possible? The matter is to be understood thus. Whatever dies by its own nature has its end according to predestation, and as the pleasure and dispensation of God arranges. But this, too, happens from different diseases and accidents, and herefrom there is no resuscitation, nor is there any preservative which can be used against predestination and the cognate end of life. But what is mortified can be resuscitated and revivified, as may be proved by many arguments which we will set down at the end of this book. So, then, there is the greatest difference between dying and mortifying, nor should it be thought that these are only two names for one thing. In very deed these differ as widely as possible. Examine the case of a man who has died by a natural and predestined death. What further good or use is there in him? None. Let him be cast to the worms. But the case is not the same with a man who has been slain with a sword or has died some violent death. The whole of his body is useful and good, and can be fashioned into the most valuable *mumia*. For though the spirit of life has gone forth from such a body, still the balsam remains, in which life is latent, which also, indeed, as a balsam conserves other human bodies. So, too, in the instance of metals you see that when a metal has a tendency to die it begins to be affected with rust, and that which has been so affected is dead; and when the whole of the metal is consumed with rust the whole is dead, and such rust can never be brought back to be a metal, but is mere ashes and no metal. It is dead, and death is in itself: nor has it any longer the balsam of life, but has perished in itself.

I. xi. 343-4

14.10

BOOK IX
CONCERNING THE SIGNATURE OF NATURAL THINGS

In this book, our first business, as being about to philosophize, is with the signature of things, as, for instance, to set forth how they are signed, what signator exists, and how many signs are reckoned. Be it known, first of all, then, that signs are threefold. The first things signed man signs; the second *Archeus* signs; the third the stars of the supernaturals. In this way, then, only three signators exist, man, *Archeus*, and the stars. Moreover, it should be remarked that the signs signed by man carry with them perfect knowledge and judgement of occult things, as well as acquaintance with their powers and hidden faculties.

The signs of the stars give prophecies and presages. They

point out the force of supernatural things, and put forth true judgements and disclosures in geomancy, chiromancy, hydromancy, pyromancy, necromancy, astronomy, the Berillistic art, and other astral sciences.

Now, in order that we may explain all the signs as correctly and as briefly as possible, it is above all else necessary that we put forward those whereof man is the signator. When these are understood you will more rightly attain to the others, whether natural or supernatural. For instance, it is known that Jews wear a yellow sign on their cloak or on their coat. What is this but a sign by which anybody who meets him may understand that he is a Jew? So, too, the lictor is known by his particoloured tunic or armlet. So, too, every magistracy decks its ministers with its own proper colours and adornments.

The mechanic marks his work with its peculiar sign, so that everyone may understand who has produced it. For what purpose does the courier carry the insignia of his master or his city on his garment, except that it may be clear he is a messenger, that he serves one or another, that he comes from one place or another, and so thus procures for himself a safe passage?

So, too, the soldier carries a sign or symbol, black, white, green, blue, or red, that he may be distinguished from the enemy. Hence it is known that one is on the side of Caesar, or of the kings; that one is an Italian, another a Gaul, etc. These are signs which relate to rank and office; and many more of them might be enumerated.

I. xi. 373-4

14.11

CONCERNING THE ASTRAL SIGNS IN THE PHYSIOGNOMY OF MAN

The signs of physiognomy derive their origin from the higher stars... The wise man can dominate the stars, and is not subjet to them. Nay, the stars are subject to the wise man, and are forced to obey him, not he the stars. The stars compel and coerce the animal man, so that where they lead he must follow, just as a thief does the gallows, a robber the wheel, a fisher the fishes, a fowler the birds, and a hunter the wild beasts. What other

reason is there for this, save that man does not know or estimate himself or his own powers, or reflect that he is a lesser
universe, and has the whole firmament with its powers hidden within himself? Thus man is called animal and unwise and
the slave of all earthly things, when, nevertheless, he received
from God in Paradise the privilege of ruling over and dominat-
ing all other creatures, and not of obeying them. So it was that
God created man last, when all other things had been made
before him. This right was afterwards lost by the Fall. Yet, the
wisdom of man was not made servile, nor did he lose his freedom. It is right, then, that the stars should follow him and obey
him, not he the stars. . . .

In order to grasp these things it must be remembered that
stars are of two kinds, terrestrial and celestial. The former belong
to folly, the latter to wisdom. And as there are two worlds,
the lesser and the larger, and the lesser rules the larger, so also
the star of the microcosm governs and subdues the celestial
star. God did not create the planets and stars with the intention that they should dominate man, but that they, like other
creatures, should obey him and serve him. And although the
higher stars do give the inclination, and, as it were, sign man
and other earthly bodies for the manner of their birth, yet that
power and that dominion are nothing, save only a predestined
mandate and office, in which there is nothing occult or abstruse
remaining, but the inner force and power is put forth through
the external signs.

But to return to our proposition concerning the physical signs
of men: know that these are twofold, like indeed in outward
form, but dissimilar in power and effect. Some are from the
upper stars of heaven; others from the lower stars of the microcosm. Every superior star signs according to birth up to mid-
age. That signature is predestined, and is not without its own
peculiar force. It is attested by a man's nature and condition
of life. But whatever the lower star of the microcosm signs from
birth has it origin from the father and the mother, as often as
the mother affects by her imagination or appetite, her fear or
dread, the unborn child in her body with supernatural signs
by means of their own close contact. These are called mothers'
marks, or uterine marks. We have spoken of these before, so

spare ourselves the labour of repetition, since it is our purpose
to treat of physiognomical signs alone, among which we understand those signs of men the like whereof neither the father
nor the mother have borne in their body. Of this class are black
or grey eyes, too small or too large; a long, crooked, or sharp-
pointed nose; hollows in the jaws, high cheekbones, a flat or
broad nose, small or large ears, a long neck, an oblong face,
a mouth large and drawn down; hair thick or fine, abundant
or scanty, black, yellow, or red, etc. Of these signs, if one or
more appear in a man, be sure that he will not lack the qualities signified thereby. Only you must judge them according
to the rules of physiognomy, and have had experience in the
art of signature, according to which you can judge a man by
outward signs.

Descending, then, to the practical portion of our subject, let
us repeat a few of these signs and their signification.

Black eyes not only denote a healthy constitution, but also,
for the most part, a constant mind free from doubt and fear,
healthy and hearty, truthful and loving virtue.

Grey eyes are the sign of a crafty man, ambiguous and incon-
sistent. Weak eyes denote good counsels, clever and profound
deliberations, and so on. Bright eyes, which turn up, down,
and to both sides, denote a false, clever man, who cannot be
deceived, faithless, shirking work, desirous of ease, seeking to
gain his livelihood in laziness, by gambling, usury, impurity,
theft, and the like.

Small eyes, somewhat deeply sunk, indicate weak sight, and
often impending blindness in old age. At the same time, they
denote brave men, bellicose, crafty, and adroit, factious, capable of enduring misfortune, and whose departure from life is,
for the most part, of a tragic character.

Large eyes denote a greedy, voracious man, especially if they
project far out of the head.

Eyes which are constantly winking indicate weak sight, a
timid and careful man. Eyes which move quickly hither and
thither, under the glance of men, indicate an amorous heart,
provident, and of quick invention.

Eyes continually cast down show a reverential and modest
man.

Red eyes show a bold, brave man.

Glittering eyes, which do not move readily, point out a hero, a high-minded, brave, quick man, formidable to his foes.

Large ears indicate good hearing, retentive memory, attention, diligence, a healthy brain and head.

I. xi. 377-82

14.12

CONCERNING THE ASTRAL SIGNS OF CHIROMANCY

Concerning the signs of chiromancy it should be held that they arise from the higher stars of the seven planets, and all of them ought to be learnt and judged from the seven planets. Now, chiromancy is a science which not only inspects the hands of men, and from their lines and wrinkles makes its judgement, but, moreover, it also considers all herbs, woods, flints, earths, and rivers—in a word, whatever has lines, veins, and wrinkles.

I. xi. 384

14.13

CONCERNING MINERAL SIGNS

Minerals and metals, apart from fire and dry material, show their indications and signs which they have received at once from the *Archeus* and from the higher stars, each one telling its genus by differences of colour and of earth. The mineral of gold differs from the mineral of silver. So the mineral of silver differs from the mineral of copper. The mineral of copper differs from the mineral of iron. So also that of iron from that of tin and of lead. And so with the rest. None can deny, then, that by means of chiromancy all minerals and metallic bodies of mines, which lie hid in secret places of the earth, may be known from their external signs. That is the chiromancy of mines, veins, and lodes, by which not only those things which are hidden within are brought forth, but also the exact depth and richness of the mine and yield of metal are made manifest. Now, in this chiromancy three things are necessary to be known, the age, depth, and breadth of the veins, as was said just now in the case of herbs. For the older its veins, the richer and more abundant in metals is the mine . . .

In pursuit of our present purpose, then, I pass on to a very brief practical exposition concerning the chiromancy of mines. The deeper and broader the veins are, the older they may be known to be. When the tracts of the veins are stretched to a very long distance, and then gape, it is a bad sign. For as the courses of the veins gape, so the mines themselves gape, which fact they indicate by their depth. Although sometimes good mines are found with a very deep descent, they for the most part vanish more and more, so that they cannot be worked without great expenditure of toil. But where those veins are increased by other accessory ones, or in any other way are frequently cut off, that is a fortunate sign, indicating that the mines are good not only on the surface, but that they increase in depth and are multiplied, so that they are rendered rich mines, and yield most ample treasure.

I. xi. 387-9

14.14

CONCERNING CERTAIN PARTICULAR SIGNS OF NATURAL AND SUPERNATURAL THINGS

We must now, in due course, speak of some peculiar signs, concerning which nothing up to this time has been handed down. In this treatise it will be very necessary that you who boast your skill in the science of signatures, who also wish to be yourselves called signators, should rightly understand what we say. In this place we are not going to speak theoretically, but practically, and we will put forth our opinion comprised in the fewest possible words for your comprehension.

First of all, know that the signatory art teaches how to give true and genuine names to all things. All of these Adam the Protoplast truly and entirely understood. So it was that after the Creation he gave its own proper name to everything, to animals, trees, roots, stones, minerals, metals, waters, and the like, as well as to other fruits of the earth, of the water, of the air, and of the fire. Whatever names he imposed upon these were ratified and confirmed by God. Now these names were based upon a true and intimate foundation, not on mere opinion, and were derived from a predestined knowledge, that is to say, the signatorial art. Adam is the first signator.

Indeed, it cannot be denied that genuine names flow forth from the Hebrew language, too, and are bestowed upon each thing according to its nature and condition. The names which are given in the Hebrew tongue indicate by their mere bestowal the virtue, power, and property of the very thing to which they belong. So when we say, 'This is a pig, a horse, a cow, a bear, a dog, a fox, a sheep, etc.,' the name of a pig indicates a foul and impure animal. A horse indicates a strong and patient animal; a cow, a voracious and insatiable one; a bear, a strong, victorious, and untamed animal; a fox, a crafty and cunning animal; a dog, one faithless in its nature; a sheep, one that is placid and useful, hurting no one. Hence it happens that sometimes a man is called a pig on account of his sordid and piggish life; a horse, on account of his endurance, for which he is remarkable beyond all else; a cow, because he is never tired of eating and drinking, and his stomach knows no moderation; a bear, because he is bigger and stronger than other people; a fox, because he is versatile and cunning, accommodating himself to all, and not easily offending anybody; a dog, because he is not faithful to anything beyond his own mouth, and shows himself unaccommodating and faithless to all; or a sheep, because he hurts nobody but himself, and is of more use to anyone else than to himself.

Then, again, many herbs and roots got their names, not from any one inborn virtue and faculty, but also from their figure, form, and appearance, as the Morsus Diaboli, Pentaphyllum, Cynoglossum, Ophioglossum, Hippuris, Hepatica, Buglosum, Dentaria, Calcatrippa (*consolida regalis*), Perforata, Satyrion or Orchis, Victorialis, Syderica, Petfoliata, Prunella, Heliotrope, and many others which need not be recounted here, but separately in the Herbary.

But, moreover, there are other signs which are worthy of our wonder, when, for example, the *Archeus* is the signator and signifies on the umbilical cord of the foetus by means of knots, from which it can be told how many children the mother has had or will have.

The same signator signs the horns of the stag with branches by which its age is known. As many branches as the horns have, so many years old is the stag. Since there is an addition of a new branch to the horn every year, the age of the stag can be set down as twenty or thirty years.

So, too, the signator marks the horns of the cow with circles from which it is known how many calves she has borne. Every circle indicates one calf.

The same signator thrusts out the first teeth of the horse so that for the first seven years its age can be certainly known from its teeth. When the horse is first born it has fourteen teeth, of which it sheds two every year, so in seven years all of them fall out. For this reason a horse more than seven years old can only be judged by one who is very skilled and practised.

The same signator marks the beak and talons of a bird with particular signs, so that every practised fowler can judge its age from these.

The same signator marks the tongues of pigs with blisters, by which their impurity can be known. If the tongue is foul, so is the whole body.

The same signator marks the clouds with different colours, whereby the tempests of the sky can be prognosticated.

So also he signs the circle of the moon with distinct colours, each one of which has its own special interpretation. Redness generally indicates coming wind; greenness or blackness, rain. The two mixed, wind with rain. At sea this is a sign which generally portends tempests and storms. Brightness and clear whiteness are a good sign, especially on the ocean. For the most part they presage quiet and serene weather.

I. xi. 397–400

15

ARCHIDOXIS MAGICA (*c.* 1570)

[Although attributed to Paracelsus, this work was most probably written by Gerhard Dorn, the prominent Paracelsist, or
one of his followers, around 1570. The use of the word 'Archidoxis' in its title was a convenient ploy to present the text as
a newly discovered occult variant of the famous 1526 work.
However, the *Archidoxis magica* reads as a typical sixteenth-
century magical text full of remedies and practices based on
astrology and sympathetic magic without any resemblance to
its earlier namesake. Johannes Huser regarded the text as
authentic and included it in his standard edition of Paracelsus'
collected works at the end of the sixteenth century. The work
is included in this anthology on the historical grounds that it
traditionally represented the 'magical' Paracelsus to earlier
generations.]

15.1

When these writings of ours come to light, many people will
doubtless be amazed at the miraculous powers inherent in
metals, which can be prepared by hand. These things will be
reckoned superstitions, sorcery, and contrary to nature; it will
be thought that they are idolatrous practices and that diaboli-
cal conjurations are required for their accomplishment. People
will say, how can it be possible that metals engraved with
characters, letters, and words could have this power, unless they

were made and prepared with sorcery and the aid of the devil? We answer thus: You seem to believe in these powers and virtues, if the devil's aid is involved; but you cannot believe that the creator of Nature, God in heaven, has as much power and could give such powers and virtues to the metals, roots, herbs, stones, and such like. Thus you appear to think the devil more powerful, artful, and almighty than the one eternal, omnipotent and merciful God who created all these metals, stones, herbs, roots, and such like, and all things which live or move in or upon the earth, water, and air for the use and benefit of mankind. But it is certain and experience teaches that the changes of time have great power and effect, particularly in several metals which are produced at special times, as is well known and which we have experienced in many ways and forms. No one can claim that the metals are dead and lifeless. For these metals contain oils, salts, sulphurs, and quintessences, which are the supreme preservatives, and have the greatest virtue to nourish human life and surpass all other simples, as we will show in all our remedies.

I. xiv. 437

15.2

If there was no life [in the metals], how could they help diseased and decayed bodies and limbs by stirring up a vital and physical energy therein, as in the case of contractures, paralysis, stone, the French Disease, dropsy, epilepsy, frenzy, and gout, and all the other diseases which I omit to mention for the sake of brevity? Therefore I say that the metals and stones have life in them just as roots, herbs, and other fruits, though of different kinds according to the time of the metal's preparation. For the time itself has a certain power which is obvious from many arguments and which we do not need to report, since they are so commonly known. For it is not our intention to describe things which are commonly known, but things which are difficult, inconceivable, and contrary to the evidence of our senses.

I. xiv. 437-8

15.3

Characters, letters, and signs each have their own virtue. When the nature of the metals, the influence and operation of the heavens and the planets, and the significance and properties of the characters, signs, and letters, and the observation of the times, hours, and days, concur and agree, who should be surprised that this manufactured sign or sigil has a virtue and operation, one for the head, being prepared in his time; another for the the sight, another for the kidney-stones, each one being prepared in his own proper time; and that they help such things and no others. But all this should be done with the help and assistance of the father of all medicine, Jesus Christ, the one and only healer.

I. xiv. 438

15.4

Against the Falling Sickness [epilepsy]
Establish the signs of the falling; whether [the fits] occur at the same hours and days in the month, how often, with regular or irregular frequency; and whether a little while before the fit [the patient] experiences slight giddiness or suddenly falls to the ground; which being perceived, if they fall at certain times and hours, then the fit does not take them suddenly. But if it comes at unequal times and hours, the contrary is true and the attack is abrupt and sudden. The first kind, when there is slight giddiness before the fit, is fatal. But if the fit is sudden, the disease is not so dangerous but more curable. The former is natural, the latter does not proceed from nature and is less weakening. The first brings frenzy and madness, but the latter does not and can be helped thus:

First, consider on what day and at what hour he fell the last time and write it down. Then see what planet rules that hour; you should also note in which sign and degree the Moon was at that time. Then the age and sex of the patient are to be noted. Now begin and give this medicine each morning: 5 drops of the spirit of vitriol, 5 drops of the quintessence of antimony, 4 drops of the quintessence of pearl. Put these in a beaker full of good rose-water and give it every morning to the paroxys-

mal and let him fast for four hours afterwards; do this for
twenty-nine days, and in the meantime prepare the lamen.

Recipe: 1 loth of fine gold and when the Moon stands in
the twelfth degree of Cancer, melt the gold in a crucible and
pour it into pure clean water. As soon as there is a conjunction
of two planets in the heavens, melt this gold again, and at the
very point of conjunction, pour into the crucible 1 loth of fine
silver, so that there is an equal mixture of gold and silver. Pour
this out and beat it into a thin plate, a hand's breadth across,
and then cut it into the form of a triangle, as appears in this
figure.

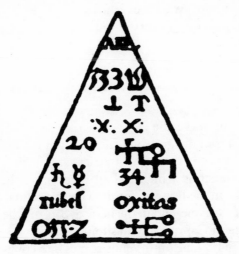

Heat this lamen very hot and let it lie until the Moon stands
in the same sign and degree that she was at the time of the [last]
fit. In the same hour engrave or draw these characters, signs,
and letters (as above) on the lamen made of gold and silver.
But you should make haste to complete the engraving in the
aforesaid hour, for otherwise it would be in vain. You should
first engrave the sign of the planet of the hour in which the
fit occurred in the middle of the lamen. The figure here was
made for Jacob Seitz at the court of the Prince of Salzburg,
and his fit occurred in the hour of Mercury. Make the other
signs as shown in the figure, except that for a woman, instead
of this character ⚹, you shall put such a one ⚶. And the
age of the patient is to given at the place where you see 34

in the figure, for the aforesaid Jacob Seitz was so many years old. Therefore the number of years is to be put in the figure corresponding to his age.

When the figure is ready, you should shave the hair on the crown of the patient's head corresponding to the size of the lamen. As soon as a fit occurs and he is still prone, pour some of the arcanum previously described into his mouth, and hold him, so that it goes down, and then lay the lamen with the script upon the naked head and have it bound on and let the patient quietly sleep. Without doubt he will never have another fit, although he might have suffered from the disease for thirty years. But let him always wear the lamen on his head and shave his head at the end of every month, in the same place where he was first shaven.

I. xiv. 441-2

15.5

A figure to preserve the sight

Make thee a round sign from finest lead in the hour of Venus when the Moon is the sign of Aries, and in that same hour engrave these signs which follow hereafter. Afterwards you should make in the hour of Saturn a copper lamen of the same size as the leaden one, and in the hour of Saturn when the Moon is in the sign of Capricorn you should engrave these signs and then let them both lie until Venus comes into conjunction with Saturn. Then, in that hour and the point of conjunction bring

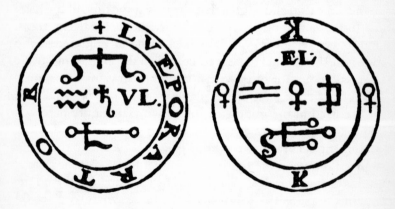

both the figures together, so that the characters and signs touch each other, then seal it with wax, in order that they will not become moist, and sew them in a little silken cloth and hang it around the neck of the patient in the hour of Mercury on a Wednesday. This restores the sight of the eyes and prevents pain and disease. It preserves the sight in old age, just as it was in youth.

I. xiv. 442-3

16

LIBER AZOTH SIVE DE LIGNO ET LINEA VITAE (1590)

[This is another spurious work, first published in Huser's quarto edition of the collected works. The connection with Paracelsus' own writings is tenuous and relates to his mention of Adam's lost *lignum vitae* (Tree of Life) and a line or cleft mark upon his visage which signified his mortality in *The Book of Long Life* (I. iii. 229). The text is not typically cabbalistic inasmuch as there is no discussion of the Tree of Life with its *sefiroth*, but its focus on man as a book of letters, numbers, and measures does indicate an unmistakable Jewish mystical influence. Cabbala had entered German intellectual life through the works of the humanist Johann Reuchlin (1455-1522). *Liber Azoth* shows how those interested in cabbalism at the end of the sixteenth century sought parallels in the writings of Paracelsus. It will be clear from the text that while its concepts are Paracelsian, their presentation and the style of the piece itself do not record the genuine voice of Paracelsus. The text is included here only on historical grounds and for the sake of comparison with authentic works.]

16.1

Whoever desires to know the secrets of all occult things should seek them nowhere else but in the Lord God, for the reason that no one can better reveal all secrets to the seeker than He

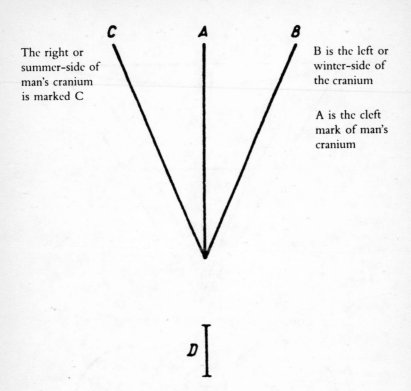

The right or summer-side of man's cranium is marked C

B is the left or winter-side of the cranium

A is the cleft mark of man's cranium

who is the originator of all secrets and arts, both heavenly and mundane.

One must first draw attention to the book in which the letters of the secrets are clearly written for all to see and understand, and one can discover everything one may wish to know written by the finger of God in this very book ... All other books are but dead letters in comparison with this book if it be read properly. Man alone is this book in which all secrets are written; but the interpreter of this book is God.

Man is characterized by the sign D [in the figure] and this is the starting point of our enquiry ... Because no fire can burn without air, we must talk about the element Fire, which is a spirit body or the house of the soul. And this fire is the true man who is the subject of our whole philosophy ... Thus I understand such burning as life, and when I say something cannot burn, I mean it cannot live.

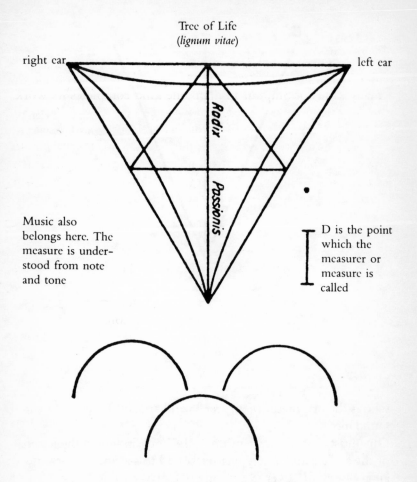

The upper stroke called *lignum vitae* is an air-door and orifice for the breath, that is the breath of life ... Now I want to show that such life or fire, that is the spirit body, is created from a threefold fire: the fire of Sulphur, the fire of Salt, and the fire of Mercury. For such fire must have threefold substance from the *Iliaster.*

Iliaster is the prime matter, from which Salt, Sulphur, and Mercury are made. By that we understand how the word FIAT was made a material and tangible body, in which all predestinations are contained and lie hidden ...

I. xiv. 547-9

16.2

De ligno et linea vitae per △ ternarium

Know therefore this philosophy. The Sulphur is *lignum vitae* and makes the *linea vitae* in man and outside man. There are many kinds of Sulphur in man: one kind completes its work in the east; a second kind found in man operates in the west; the third is effective towards midnight; the fourth towards noon. For this reason I will begin with the *linea vitae* and *lignum* around noon and the great cleft mark on the forehead of man. Such a cleft mark is not only found on the human cranium but also in all plants and elements. There is also a line in water, which we call *ileida*, where two waters cleave and form a line as in the sea. The rainbow in the air and fire is a similar phenomenon . . . In all plants the line is towards noon, but not always occidental, oriental, or septentrional . . . The fishes bear their *linea vitae*, you may see it behind their heads. Wild animals bear the fiery cleft, while game birds have two clefts, one on the head, another at their tail. The peacock demonstrates this with his rainbow colours and when he spreads his tail . . . And thus all colours, all kinds of flowers, are nothing but an intimation of the terrestrial cleft and the rainbow. A flower indicates by its number of petals the region in which it belongs; thus a five-petal flower or its virtue belongs in the *quinarium* . . . Thus cabbala will determine the hierarchy wherein three matches three, four four, five five, and every number in the heavens. Cabbala is the consideration of the *linea vitae* and the notion of measure.

I. xiv. 558-60

16.3

Practica lineae vitae

In the preceding chapter it was explained that man was born from three [matrices], the macrocosm, the microcosm of Adam, and the microcosm of Eve. Take the matrix of the macrocosm first, for I want to describe the material *limbus* which God has planted in the matrix of the microcosm. For God took the same seed from the Elements all over the whole world to *one* place and created man from it; this act occurred on the water. Water is the matrix of the macrocosm. In addition there were the heavens, and Adam and Eve were created in this heaven from a *limbus*, which was composed of many thousand pieces, materials and virtues . . . Just like a circle, carved on a flat surface, which has a point in its centre

and many lines radiating from this point to the circumference— the lines all lead to *one* point. Thus God took all the virtues from all living and moving creatures and made *one* thing and *one* virtue of them, namely Adam. These virtues thus became by means of the word FIAT *one* piece, which is called AZOT and was ♠ [Sulphur], ♯ [Salt] and ☿ [Mercury] . . .

All Sulphur wishes to rise. Because it is a fiery body and can be best observed in the fire, it always tends to rise. This 'upwards' should be understood by means of this figure:

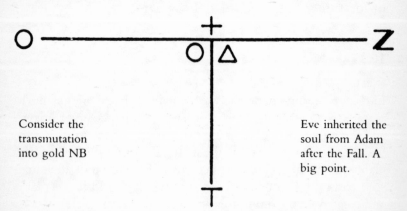

Consider the transmutation into gold NB

Eve inherited the soul from Adam after the Fall. A big point.

NB. ○Ƶ is the *linea vitae* which runs from the left to the right ear in man. ⊤△ is the *linea vitae* from the nose to the middle of the preceding line, the trival line. Thus three lines proceed from one point, Ƶ to the left, ○ to the right, and a third in the centre. Therefore look at these forms:

Here the ternarius is open, that is in Adam. This should be open and not covered in honour of God.

The ternarius is closed on the front of woman's head ⊕ and open at the rear. If that were not so, no one would die a mortal death . . .

I. xiv. 572-4

SOURCES AND BIBLIOGRAPHY

A. PRIMARY SOURCES

Individual works of Paracelsus were published during his lifetime and in subsequent decades of the sixteenth century. The
first collected edition was *Erster [- Zehender] Theil der Bücher und
Schrifften . . . Philippi Theophrasti Bombast von Hohenheim, Paracelsi
genannt*, edited by Johannes Huser, 10 vols., quarto (Basle, 1589-
91) and a folio edition in two volumes at Strasburg in 1603.
These works contained the original Early New High German
and Latin texts of Paracelsus and his assistants. This remained
the most complete text of Paracelsus' writings until the publication of the Sudhoff–Matthiessen edition of the Early New
High German and Latin texts in the early twentieth century.
This edition has been used in the preparation of the *Essential
Readings*.

The references in the *Essential Readings* relate to the part, volume,
and page numbers in the Sudhoff–Matthiessen and Goldammer editions where the original passage may be found:

Paracelsus. Sämtliche Werke, edited by Karl Sudhoff and Wilhelm
Matthiessen.
Part I: Medizinische, naturwissenschaftliche und philosophische
   Schriften. Vols. vi–ix (Munich, 1922-5); Vols. i–v, x–xiv
   (Munich and Berlin, 1928-33).

Part II: Die theologischen und religionsphilosophischen Schriften. Vol. i (Munich, 1923).

Paracelsus. Sämtliche Werke, edited by Kurt Goldammer. Part II: Die theologischen und religionsphilosophischen Schriften. Vols. iv–vii (Wiesbaden, 1955-61); Vol. ii (Wiesbaden, 1965); Vol iii (Wiesbaden, 1986).

A convenient and accessible edition of the major writings is highly recommended to the reader of modern German: *Theophrastus Paracelsus. Werke*, edited by Will-Erich Peuckert, 5 vols. (Basle and Stuttgart, 1965-8).

There is a nineteenth-century translation into English mainly devoted to the alchemical and hermetic writings: *The Hermetic and Alchemical Writings of Paracelsus the Great*, edited by Arthur Edward Waite, 2 vols. (London, 1894). (Chapters 4 and 14 of this book have been extracted from this source.)

Two anthologies of Paracelsus' writings, arranged by themes, are also of interest: *Schriften Theophrasts von Hohenheim genannt Paracelsus*, edited by Hans Kayser (Leizig, 1921). *Paracelsus. Selected Writings*, edited by Jolande Jacobi, translated by Norbert Guterman, second edition (Princeton, N.J., 1958).

B. SECONDARY SOURCES

Debus, Allen G., *The English Paracelsians* (London, 1965).

Gray, Ronald, *Goethe the Alchemist* (Cambridge, 1952).

Hargrave, John, *The Life and Soul of Paracelsus* (London, 1951).

Hartmann, Franz, *The Life of Philippus Theophrastus, Bombast of Hohenheim etc* (London, 1887).

Kaiser, Ernst, *Paracelsus. Mit Selbstzeugnissen und Bilddokumenten* (Hamburg, 1969).

Pagel, Walter, *Paracelsus: an introduction to philosophical medicine in the era of the Renaissance*, second edition (Basle, 1982).

Shumaker, Wayne, *The Occult Sciences in the Renaissance* (Berkeley, California, 1972).

Stoddart, Anna M., *The Life of Paracelsus* (London, 1911).
Telepnef, Basilio de, *Paracelsus: a genius amidst a troubled world* (St Gallen, [1945]).
Vickers, Brian. ed., *Occult and scientific mentalities in the Renaissance* (Cambridge, 1984).

INDEX